S A F E T Y   L   E   A   D

Safety Lead

From virtual safety to rea

C000176776

The other Hollin Books are:

Power Coaching

The Too Busy Trap

The Steps Before Step One

Notes on Behavioural Management Techniques

Ideas For Wimps

How To Escape From Cloud Cuckoo Land

How To Empty The Too Hard Box

Behavioural Coaching

Behavioural Safety for Leaders

BMT Scorecards

Many thanks to everyone who influenced and contributed to this book. Thanks to Craig Reade, Andy Bull, Aaron Sorkin, Jack Sheehan, Dr Marshall Goldsmith, Phil Risbridger, Simon Roberts, Sir Ken Robinson, Richard Kazbour, Ryan Olson, James Dobson, Iain Humphreys, Bob Cummins, Dr John Austin, Peter Farrer, Neil Park, Dr Bill Hopkins, Lisa Kazbour, Alasdair Cathcart, Manny Rodriguez, Ian Galloway OBE, Dr Bill Redmon, Dr Bill Abernathy, Dr Aubrey Daniels, F.W. Taylor, Dr Charles Handy CBE, Bruce Faulkner and Alan Cheung. Special thanks to the Hollin team: Joanne, Rachel, Nicola, Jean, Alison, Claire and Dave. Extra special thanks to Lynn Dunlop for some of the longest editing rallies ever performed in the history of Hollin books.

Hollin Ltd
Westminster House
10 Westminster Road
Macclesfield
Cheshire
SK10 1BX
howard@hollin.co.uk

First published by Hollin Ltd August 2017
© Copyright 2017 Hollin Ltd

Graphics by Creative Hero
ISBN number 978-0-9575211-4-8

Foreword

by Andrew Bull, BEng, CEng, FICE, FIOD.

This is a great book, one that I am very happy to endorse, and I would encourage you to set aside time to read it and follow up with an implementation plan.

It's strategic, scientific and the concepts are simple enough to be implemented by normal people on everyday projects.

Safety performance has plateaued in many organisations over the past several years, so to drive further improvements we need to start trying some new approaches. This book provides suggestions and ideas that you could adopt without fear of appearing reckless or too radical.

It gives practical suggestions for individuals to adopt and develop their personal safety leadership, but goes beyond regurgitating what has already been published on the subject and is a thoughtful leadership piece in terms of moving the safety agenda forward. Howard uses a scientific approach, but at the same time keeps it very simple. Please don't dismiss something just because it appears simple - simple suggestions mean they can be conveyed and implemented with reasonable consistency to make a meaningful difference. Remember, complexity is the enemy of execution.

I've worked with Howard for many years and those familiar with him will know that his coaching style is often to push people beyond the personal boundaries of what they would ever normally consider doing, and then dial back the suggestions until agreement is found on something that could be tried.

I have been party to those conversations where I've thought, "This is going too far - I won't get away with this and it won't be received well." The message just feels too far away from the recipient's norms of acceptability. This is always a difficult balance when trying to make progress in any subject area - if we don't push the boundaries then for sure no progress will be made at all, but push the boundaries too far and the suggestion becomes too different, too scary, too difficult for most people to conceive adoption of the proposed change. I think that Howard has pitched the content of this book just right.

No matter what level you are operating at, I would encourage you read this book and pick something to try out. It might be on your section, your project, your region, or across your whole business - but remember, your job is to influence those in your immediate environment. What you do and how you do it has to be adapted to the level you are working at in the organisation. If you are operating at the workface, you can have an immediate impact on the safety of those around you in the very place where injuries are most likely to happen. If you are in senior management, you cast a much broader shadow, and influence the working environment and culture across the organisation; you have a responsibility to appreciate that your actions are creating the environment that is delivering your current results. It takes a lot of discipline to focus on your own behaviours and the behaviours of those who work as your direct reports, and to ensure that they are doing what you expect of them to create an environment that supports the safe completion of task activities.

The book has been written to be accessible to all, so everyone can benefit from a safer working environment, but to skilfully implement many of the suggestions does require an understanding of behavioural science. If there are elements of the book that you don't quite understand, I would encourage you to get in touch with Howard or any of the team at Hollin who run some great courses to teach the basics, or can tailor more advanced courses and coaching sessions to support you with a bespoke implementation plan for your business or project(s).

If you can find the time to sit back and observe what is currently happening across your organisation, where the energy and effort is being consumed and then carry out a simple analysis for the question, "Is this activity making our workplace safer or not?" you will soon start to see the vast amount of distractions that are created with good intention, but no longer serve a useful purpose. As Howard says, like training wheels on a bicycle, they may have served you well at a time when you needed them, but in the longer term they could be holding you back.

As a final note, reading this book will hopefully give you some new knowledge, but this in itself won't make any difference to your current workplace. You need to take an idea and implement it to make a real difference – go on, give it a go – you might just make a positive difference to your workplace.

Andrew Bull,
Verwood, Dorset, England,
August 2017

Contents

1. Introduction

Safety Leadership looks at where the field of safety is now, and examines why many current approaches are not necessarily making workplaces more safe. The book examines safety from a leadership point of view, arguing that the time is right to approach safety with the rigour of science, and making suggestions for how to do this. It is structured chronologically, dealing with the past, then the progression of the science, and finishing with suggestions for solutions. If you want to start with the solutions then steam on to Part II; it's entirely your call.

I wrote this serious book with a nod to irony and with some mild doses of verbal mischief. It's my therapy for dealing with some of the more dubious business leaders out there who don't know how to create safe working environments for their people. I am sure all the excellent leaders who do know how to create a safe place for their workers will find ideas in this book that can make things even better for them than they are now.

This book deals with:
* Safety history - how did we get here?
* What problems exist now
* Scientific solutions for safety
* Next steps

I will explain why a scientific approach should be used by organisational leaders and outline what a scientific approach looks like. I've also written about the knowledge and training required to get to the next steps. The book outlines a performance framework to help organisational leaders design a strategic and measurable approach to organisational safety.

Many leaders are aware of behavioural-based safety, or BBS, but this book is not about that. BBS is briefly addressed in chapter 5, but it is distinct from the approach advocated here.

1.1 A Note On Language

Sometimes bad things happen to good words. The word 'behaviour' is sat there in its rightful place in the dictionary. Its scientific definition is 'what people do and say'. This definition is simple enough to understand and I, for one, am very happy with it. Unfortunately its non-scientific usage can be a little confusing.

One of the biggest problems with the word 'behaviour' occurs when people use subjective terms but call them behaviours. True behaviours are entirely objective. It is common to see lists of so-called behaviours in organisations - these often include 'communicating' or 'trust'. These are not true behaviours, as they are subjective.

'Behaviour' has also been used as a descriptor for physical events; e.g. 'The car behaved erratically' - cars cannot 'behave' in our objective behavioural science world. I think it's worth being a stickler on the scientific definition of the word. It helps tremendously when working to understand why people do what they do.

Behavioural Safety expert Dr Scott Geller has argued for many years that the terminology used in the safety arena is misleading and distracting. The words used when speaking about safety have great power to steer the narrative. Safety terminology should reflect the belief behind creating a safe place for people to work.

The use of the word 'accident' for example can create a feeling that an injury sustained was unavoidable. Here is a short list of changes that will not only make much more sense to everyone, but will also help improve the way safety is perceived throughout organisations. The list is taken from the Hollin booklet *Behavioural Safety for Leaders* (2011):

Injury and incident, NOT accident
'Accident' is the wrong word. Dr Scott Geller makes the point that an accident is something that people had no influence over or involvement in causing. Most injuries and incidents occur in situations which are planned and involve humans behaving. Human

behaviour is the primary contributory factor in almost all incidents
and injuries. Genuine accidents in the safety field are rare events.

Zero is a vision, NOT a goal
Stating that zero injuries is a goal is just a millstone around everyone's
neck. Sometimes people pay themselves bonuses to achieve various
states of zero injury. This shows a lack of understanding that the goal
is to create a safe place for people to work. Once the threat of someone
losing a bonus comes into play then all kinds of avoidance behaviours
could ensue. To succeed, zero injuries needs to be a vision, not a
numbers game. See chapter 6.5 for more on 'zero' targets.

Safety is a value, NOT a priority
Safety cannot be a priority, it must be a value, and it must be the
foundation on which everything else is based. Saying it's a priority is
to ignore the reality that day-to-day conversations on other topics
(production, quality, customers, etc.) take place more frequently in
workplaces. Priorities change; values remain.

An injury is a chance to learn, NOT punish
There has been an increase in out-of-proportion leadership responses
when an injury or incident occurs. It could be predicated on the
'bonus for safety' culture which exists in some organisations, or
simply stem from a desire to be seen to act following an injury. In
either case, this kind of reaction always makes the future less safe
rather than more safe. Leadership behaviours that deliver punishing
consequences after an injury create all kinds of future avoidance
behaviour from the very people that need to be more open about what
is happening in the workplace. If leaders respond angrily when they
hear bad news, the likelihood of them hearing bad news in the future
reduces. Most leaders understand that there should be 'consequences'
after an injury or incident has occurred, but some fall into the trap of
simply attempting to punish an evident unwanted behaviour. It is
important to learn how different consequences can and will drive
different future behaviours - both desired and undesired.

See Appendix C for more information about the words used in this book.

1.2 Glossary Of Behavioural Science Terminology

Behavioural Science Term	Brief Explanation (See Appendix C for in-depth explanation)
Antecedent	An attempt to prompt a behaviour.
Behaviour	What someone says or does.
BMT	Behavioural Management Techniques: A unique blend of applied behavioural science tools and project management skills.
Consequences	What happens after a behaviour, always from the point of view of the performer of the behaviour.
Environment	The room, factory floor, site, the immediate surroundings, including the people in that space.
Reinforcement	When a behaviour has been reinforced, the performer is likely to repeat that behaviour again in the future - either because they want to or because they feel they have to. This is always from the point of view of the performer.
Positive reinforcement	When the performer does more of a behaviour because they enjoy the reinforcement - they 'want to'.
Negative reinforcement	When the performer does more of a behaviour in order to escape or avoid a threat - they feel they 'have to'.
Punishment	When a behaviour has been punished, the performer is unlikely to do that behaviour again in the future. This is always from the point of view of the performer.

Part I
2. The Safety Story So Far

I started work in 1969. In my second job after school I was employed as a trainee technician working for the local authority in the drainage section. I was sent out on site to a quite complex tunnel project. The ground conditions were silty and wet and compressed air was used to keep the ground stable. The contractor was Mowlem and they used a vertical air lock for access and egress for the people and materials.

I learned a lot. Well, on reflection I learned what not to get wrong, and fast. The job proceeded at a rate of knots, driven by the foreman and the amazing miners who could shovel like I had never seen before. My role was mostly to hold stuff - hold the dumb end of the tape, hold pegs while the surveyor hit them with a sledge hammer, lie in water and hold plum bobs - and mostly "Keep still until I say OK."

I also learned that there was a hierarchy on site. The site manager (agent) worked for a visiting contracts manager, but the king of the site was the foreman. Some things don't change, and the role of the foreman, frontline supervisor, works manager, site leader (whatever name you use) has not really changed. The workforce do the work, but the primary supervisor sets the workforce to work. They create and maintain the site workplace environment, including its safety; the primary supervisor is the consequence provider for everyone on site, both in theory and in most cases in practice too.

I remember the advances in technology, especially the surveying ones. We tossed away our measuring chains and marvelled at the new 'Distomat'. "You press a button and it gives you the distance?" Hard to believe at the time. These days, surveying is no human marvel; it's a technological one. Tunnelling machines have replaced shovelling miners in many cases, and every aspect of construction has benefitted from technological advances. The technological advancements have been phenomenal. It's surprising that organisations have waited so long to think about a scientific approach to how we create workplace conditions for the humans.

In the 70's I remember the emergence of the safety consultant. These people used to visit sites in the early stages of work and bring with them the 'site starter pack'. We dutifully posted our posters and filed our HSAWA forms, filled in our statutory notices: That was 'safety' to us back then. I don't remember anyone being injured apart from cuts and bruises. I do remember nearly being hit by a bag of bolts that fell down the shaft and landed next to me, and I do remember being scared when the noisy compressed air grout pan was being used in the tunnel. I remember being acutely aware of what appeared safe and not. I took my lead from the miners, gangers and foreman. I watched them climb up the bolts in the shaft but did not try it myself. I could climb a very long vertical ladder no problem; "Hold the rungs" I kept telling myself.

During the 80's seat belts in cars were introduced and the new law was heavily advertised. Initially, most people railed against wearing these uncomfortable belts. It's second nature now. On construction sites, the safety audit became more prevalent and comprised a nice person visiting site and talking to us about a bunch of stuff. They made us aware of dangerous substances, showed us how to use gas detectors, checked lifting slings and hooks; they were pleasant, and harmless. I remember the high viz vest being introduced. Many of the workforce took some persuading for sure.

In the 90s, the safety 'professional' appeared on the scene and the mood changed a bit. The law changed a few times also. The safety professional became an in-house employee quoting statutory requirements - they were a 'quoting rules and regulations' type of person.

The years from 2000 to 2012 saw a significantly lower number of injuries. Some started viewing safety as very important. Many people declared victory as injury numbers reduced. Then the graphs then began to plateau. Client organisations began to take more interest in safety as the corporate manslaughter legislation emerged. Big safety conferences began to appear, with attention-grabbing presentations by speakers who had been injured. Safety consultants appeared on the scene, promising company directors surety and protection from the new safety laws.

Behaviour-Based Safety, or BBS, emerged and was hailed as the 'next great thing' to get past the plateau and deliver zero injuries. People started to add the word 'behaviour' to their safety and other corporate programmes, but few learned about the underlying behavioural science. The word behaviour gained notoriety as seemingly everyone used it in what looks, at least in part, like a quest to add credibility. As a result of this misuse some people have now started saying, "We don't use the 'B' word anymore."

During the last decade or so there have again been reductions in incidents and injuries. Some of this improvement is due to advances in technology: Everything from the introduction of gloves that workers can comfortably carry out work whilst wearing, to the most up-to-date remotely operated machinery. Safety has improved, but not for all the reasons that some believe, and even then only modestly. A lot of organisations are improving safety slowly and claiming victory despite all of the distracting 'virtual safety' they are pushing on to their staff and workforce (see chapter 5). The downstream impact is that genuine safety improvement is moving at an ever-slowing pace.

Company directors are legally bound to improve safety but some of them, without a consistent and replicable way to do so, have simply piled initiative on initiative, process on process. Industry is flooded with attitude-changing programmes, awareness courses, IT systems for near-miss reporting, 'zero' visions, safety observations and a myriad of other well-intended but unscientific programmes to improve safety performance.

The attention paid to safety as a result of these initiatives began to bring the numbers of injuries down, but there is a problem. Data is now available that shows an overall impressive reduction in reported minor injuries over time, but those numbers have now stopped reducing. Even worse, major incidents and fatalities are maintaining their frequency.

There are so many well-intended safety processes in any given organisation that it is impossible to tell which ones work. There is an understandable but superstitious reluctance to remove any processes or initiative in case someone is injured following its removal. Some safety initiatives served companies well, but, like training wheels on a bicycle, could now be holding them back. The right thing to do is only go forward with what will really improve safety performance. Until now, safety leadership has relied upon almost a blind faith that a combination of refined processes, an educated workforce and strict supervision will prevent injuries. A change is needed. Safety is benefitting from the research emerging from the global scientific safety practitioners. It is now time to be scientific about safety performance.

3. Safety Leadership And Behavioural Science

Ensuring that there is a safe place for people to work is one of a leader's most important responsibilities, morally and legally. Leaders often receive leadership training and safety training, but the link between the two is rarely examined closely.

3.1 Safety

It is an organisation's ethical and legal responsibility to create a safe place for people to work. Parents create a safe place for their children to enjoy their lives. It is unlikely that they do this because of the laws in place regarding care. Most good organisational leaders do the same. At work, the general term 'safety', or more accurately 'occupational safety', is used in the pursuit of creating a safe place for people to work. Workplace safety is protected by law in the UK: This is the Health and Safety at Work Act 1974 (also referred to as HSWA, the HSW Act, the 1974 Act or HASAWA). It places a duty on all employers "to ensure, so far as is reasonably practicable, the health, safety and welfare at work" of all their employees.

Being safe is: 'A task executed and completed without the performer causing an incident or injury, or creating a hazard for themselves or someone else'. The focus is not on 'safety', but instead on the active behaviour of 'completing the task'. Safety initiatives or programmes will only help people to be more safe if they simultaneously facilitate those task completions. Anything that hinders task completion (including safety initiatives) will decrease the probability of it being successfully adopted. The way to successfully implement safety processes is to identify - with the person performing the task - what is required to carry out each task safely, and then ensure that the performer has all of those ingredients. What it takes to do a task safely is likely to be a combination of things, but each of these things will be specific and measurable.

Quality of work, production, and safety are all by-products of tasks being executed correctly. If the direct workplace leaders identify the ingredients required to carry out the safe execution of tasks and make sure they are in place, each worker has a better chance of working uninjured. Leaders create safe workplace environments; safe for their employees and safe for the public affected by whatever venture is occurring in their vicinity. The role of the executive leaders in the organisation is to create the right environment so that local leaders can create their own local environments for safe working.

3.2 Using Behavioural Science For Safety Leadership

The tools and techniques of behavioural science are particularly relevant to safety and safety leadership because almost all injuries and incidents in the workplace are a direct or indirect result of human behaviour. Behavioural science defines 'behaviour' as 'what people do and say'.

Behavioural Science, in simple terms, explains that humans behave in a certain way because of the consequences that they experience or believe that they will experience. These consequences are provided from their immediate surroundings (the environment). The environment often includes other people's behaviour, both now and in the past, and what happened following the behaviour.

Behavioural Science also shows that attitudes and beliefs are not major influencers in day-to-day behaviours; the workplace environment is a stronger driver of workplace behaviours. Everyone believes that people have the right to go home safely every day, and no-one comes to work with the attitude that they don't care if they suffer an injury or not, yet injuries and incidents still occur. Accepting that sustainably changing attitudes and beliefs is both difficult to do and unlikely to improve workplace safety alone can be difficult. Attribution bias describes the phenomenon where people are more likely to blame other people's attitudes for things that go wrong than they are to blame their own behaviour. This bias comes into play when discussing workplace safety, as many attempts to get workers to be more safe involve attempts to change their attitudes or beliefs. Instead, it is important to examine the local environment as the primary driver for behaviours.

By learning the principles of behavioural science it becomes possible to understand why someone is doing what they are doing, and also to predict and shape future behaviour. There is always a reason why people do what they do. Analysing the consequences that the performer may receive (or thinks they will receive) as a result of the behaviour aids understanding of what is driving the behaviour.

People have been using behavioural science to understand and shape behaviour for the last 90 years. These excellent techniques have been developed and proved over the decades. The environment that a leader creates for their workers supports the behaviours in that environment - both the desired and the undesired behaviours. In the workplace, people's behaviours are contingent on the environment created by the organisational leaders. A workplace is safe, or isn't safe, or any place in between these extremes.

A scientific approach to safety involves data. Lagging measures such as injury numbers are thankfully now scarce, so the numbers are too low to help most organisations with injury prevention. Many organisations now use close call (near miss) data, but this approach has its flaws, which are explored later. Gathering the right sort of data on the right things is vital. Many safety initiatives are expensive and time-consuming, but their efficacy is not measured rigorously. Their success is judged by a lack of injuries (see chapter 9) and by gut feel. Loss aversion and confirmation bias combine to make it unlikely that a programme, once adopted, will be dropped, regardless of how well (or not) it helps people work safely. A more rigorous approach is better: Effective leaders do not just do things and hope they work; they do things and find out if they worked and adjust as necessary.

The key to sustainable safe working is to focus on the creation of a safe working environment. This environment is primarily created by both executive and local leaders. Everything that succeeds in a workplace environment does so because of people. Everything that fails in a workplace environment does so because of people. If a behaviour is not happening, e.g. the reporting of an injury, it indicates that the consequences to the performer for the desired behaviour of 'reporting' must be perceived by them as potentially punishing. The responsibility for changing that perception falls on the leader, not the performer.

Every behaviour occurs for a reason. Scientifically, the local environmental components and contingencies align such that a behaviour occurs. Every person's behaviour is influenced by the environmental factors that surround them at the time their behaviour occurs. Scientific analysis can usually explain the components in the environment that led to an incident or injury. For every behaviour that occurs, there are antecedents; events or conditions that immediately precede the behaviour.

Not every 'unsafe' behaviour leads to an injury. An undesired behaviour can be performed numerous times without the performer suffering or causing an injury. Post-injury investigations show that in the vast majority of cases the behaviour that led to the injury had occurred before, in some cases many times before. It is useful to recognise that not all undesired behaviours lead to an injury every time (Dr Ryan Olson refers to this condition as 'the rare event trap'). This creates an obvious opportunity to observe behaviours before they result in an injury. It creates the opportunity to observe the environmental components that are supporting the current undesired behaviours.

Behaviourally speaking, 'awareness of risk' is not a motivating operation. What will motivate people to act is a perception of a threat. If an immediate and real threat is perceived, avoidance action is always taken. If, on the other hand, there is an awareness of a potential risk but it is not currently perceived as an immediate threat, the performer may continue with the task at hand. If the performer's history with this task always results in a completed task without injury, the performer will continue these behaviours. It is important to note that the perspective of the individual performer will take precedence: It is possible for two people working side-by-side to perceive vastly different threats in the same workplace environment.

A request for workers to act to avoid potential threats is an example of an antecedent. Behavioural science describes an antecedent as an attempt to drive a behaviour. Without attendant consequences, an antecedent has only a 20% chance of driving a behaviour. A speed limit sign, for example, doesn't result in reliable compliance from those on the road. A process, a rule or regulation, a sign, the law, or an email are all antecedents and on their own are weak at driving desired behaviours. Consequences (pleasant and unpleasant) are the primary motivating factors in human behaviour, and those are provided by the workplace environment, which in turn is created and supported by the leaders.

4. Virtual Safety Or Real Safety?

Whilst they are generally poor drivers of behaviour, antecedents are also necessary. Without them, people will not know what is expected of them. Relying on them alone, however, is behaviourally unsound and will not drive safe behaviours. Purely antecedent-driven safety is called 'virtual safety'.

Reliably safe behaviours in the workplace are brought about by a purposefully designed combination of antecedents and consequences. Consequences are designed into the environment by the leader and, when artfully delivered, will drive the behaviours that will keep people safe. This is called 'real safety'.

Real safety takes into account that the natural consequences of behaving safely can be punishing, and adds other consequences into the environment to counteract this effect. A leader skilled in creating real safety conditions accepts the difficulties of driving safe behaviours, and understands how important the environment is when trying to elicit safe behaviours.

4.1 Virtual Safety

Virtual safety is well-intended in the main, but it cannot keep people safe. All organisations will have a necessary degree of virtual safety, as legal requirements and governance must be met. It is important, however, to be able to identify virtual safety and to minimise the distractions caused by it wherever possible. Distractions of any kind make a workplace less safe. Common aspects of virtual safety include:

- Paperwork - some paperwork is necessary, but organisations rarely take steps to deliberately minimise paperwork for staff.
- Workplace initiatives - these are good if they work well, but are often distracting and poorly executed.

- A septic focus - where the original good intention of an initiative gets lost in policing the new procedures and attendant measures.
- Statements such as "We always…" or "We never…", which are counterproductive. This kind of language is designed to send a strong and reassuring message about safety, but its unintended impact is to reduce the integrity of the leaders from the workers' perspective.
- Believing things are safe because people have attended all the right mandatory courses, paperwork is in place and boxes have been ticked.
- Policies and procedures are in place.
- The company has safety values, and safety is first on the meeting agenda.
- There are contrived conversations about safety, 'safety moments' etc.
- Surveys reveal that safety feels patronising, going through the motions.

Virtual safety thinking suggests that if everyone complied with rules, processes and procedures, there would be no injuries or incidents. That implies that the main problem in safety is a lack of compliance. The reality, in fact, is that the rules and processes people are asked to comply with are often not fit for purpose - they are designed for a perfect world and don't take predictable human behaviours into account. The natural consequences of poorly-designed processes inevitably lead to performers undertaking unsafe behaviours.

4.2 Real Safety

Real safety occurs where leaders ensure that people have the tools, enough time and the right resources to do every task that results in a productive output. These leaders take every opportunity to provide certainty to their workplace environments. Real safety is present when:

- Staff, plant and site workers are involved in planning jobs and ordering the materials and tools.
- Everyone constantly seeks out dysfunction and addresses it.
- Safety is a product of completing a task rather than the product of a piece of paper.
- There is good planning and preparation, including the allocation of correct tools, resources and time.

- The desired behaviours are supported through peers and competent supervisory feedback.
- Supervisors and leaders regularly seek feedback and remove any barriers inhibiting the workforce.
- There is recruitment of qualified, competent people, including leaders.
- There is testing for knowledge at recruitment, inductions and reviews.
- Staff and workforce are trained in behavioural science, starting at the top.
- Simple behavioural scorecards are used.
- Work gangs talk every day with their supervisor, and review - adjusting tomorrow's plan.
- The local leaders assertively resist well-meant but misguided corporate meddling.
- Successes are celebrated.

Real safety also takes into account physiological strain on all the people in an organisation. People who are under stress, whether in their personal lives or at work, are operating with a potential distraction, and any distraction is inherently unsafe. It is vital, therefore, that leaders identify and remove any stress where they have the power to do so.

Regular anonymous surveys will reveal the available intelligence within the workplace. With that knowledge, leaders can act to reduce virtual safety and increase real safety.

5. Problems With Early Behavioural Safety Schemes (BBS)

The field of behavioural safety emerged because it was believed that 'fixing people's behaviours' would prevent injuries and incidents. Underpinning this message was the incorrect assumption that people 'behaving unsafely' is what causes injuries and incidents. This is a flawed premise, however. Injuries occur when the environment has not been set up so that a worker can complete a task without distraction. Workers can feel like they are expected to take some risks in order to complete the task. If there is a lack of tools, training, time or materials, or the worker is distracted from focusing entirely on the task, then the potential for injuries to occur increases.

Behavioural-Based Safety, or BBS as it is known in the UK, is fundamentally different from BBS in the US. Most programmes in the UK are fairly subjective psychology-based 'awareness' courses founded on looking at on attitudes and beliefs. These courses rarely teach people that the environment is key. They are not terribly effective; we have been asked to deliver our 'BMT for Safety' courses in a number of organisations that had previously sunk quite a lot of cost on what turned out to be ineffective awareness courses. The US has taken more of a scientific approach in part, and has had some success with BBS observation programmes. However, these quickly fail when they are not supported by leadership.

Over the last 15 years, many companies have embarked on a wave of behavioural safety observation schemes. Despite initial successes, many of them are now complaining that safety has not continued to improve over time, or has worsened. The reason for this is that many of the schemes ignored the scientific fact that behaviour is contingent on the real environment. People behave differently when they know they are being observed. Asking workers to observe one another in order to compete mandatory observation forms meant that the data gathered was skewed and did not reflect the reality in an unobserved environment.

Behavioural science tells us that the current environment influences our behaviour. Changes in the current environment can help create new behaviours, including safer ones. If BBS, or any safety initiative, is applied without an understanding of how the environment is currently affecting behaviour, leaders cannot be sure that the new initiative will be a positive influence, regardless of the intended impact. For example, if leaders ask workers to observe each other's behaviours in an environment that is low on trust and with poor relationships, the observation process will feel punishing and people will avoid it.

If leaders aren't well versed in how to use behavioural data and generate a positive impact, the data is likely to be used in a way that inadvertently demoralizes the workforce. If there is low engagement, workers will probably only conduct observations if there is a significant amount of coercion. Having to coerce people to engage with safety (by using either a "do this or else" approach or with incentives) does not advance the safety culture. These 'well-meant but still failed' situations occur all too often but can easily be addressed with an understanding of behavioural science.

6. What Went Wrong

Many generic safety practices exist in organisations in the developed world. A great number of them are useful. However, some are difficult to execute effectively, some waste a lot of time, some create aversive conditions, some appear at the outset like a good idea but actually create less safe conditions, and some are just massively distracting.

The data shows that minor injuries are reducing but, crucially, fatalities and major injuries are occurring at the same rate they were 20 years ago. Perhaps this is happening because people are distracted from focusing on the big issues; the things that will prevent major injuries, like proper planning, good time management and all the other essential daily behaviours that deliver successful safe business and projects.

Common safety initiatives - like reverse parking, lids on coffee cups, stair monitors or safety moments - can lull people into feeling as if they are doing their bit for safety. In the majority of cases, these are just 'easy to police' placebos: Virtual safety. It is possible that these schemes work in some environments, but there does not appear to be any data that supports these types of safety initiative when they are applied as a general rule. Implementing a new initiative is only worthwhile if it can be proven to be useful in that specific environment. Otherwise, it becomes nothing more than a distraction, and an irritating one if you have been scolded by the stair monitor whilst carrying your hot coffee up the stairs.

Apart from the inherent danger of distractions, people only have so much bandwidth for initiatives. If workers' attention is all taken with virtual safety activities then it reduces the time available for the real safety stuff; the properly planned activities with the right people and the right tools. Courageous leaders need to ask, "Have we got data that shows which of our activities genuinely improve safety?"

Over the last twenty-five years, safety seems to have become more about governance than keeping people safe. This is particularly notable in public companies, but is not limited to them. It has been well-intentioned for the most part, but it does not actually improve safety. If safety governance takes precedence over real safety, then virtual safety abounds and that means people cannot know what are expected to do when it matters. There is evidence that many workers are uncertain about their own company's determination to create safe workplaces. Many of today's safety leadership messages are mixed, i.e. 'tell us everything that goes wrong' and simultaneously 'we want zero incidents'.

Over the last ten years or so it has also become more common for leaders to want to personally demonstrate how much they care about safety. Some have gone to ridiculous lengths to demonstrate that they care. There are instances of leaders taking personal charge of an enquiry when an injury or incident does occur; this kind of rank-jumping rarely has a happy ending. It's always best to remain detached and let the professionals investigate incidents before making personal statements.

Often, when an injury occurs it prompts a bad reaction from leaders, even an over-reaction. Many organisations stop all work and take part in events that unintentionally punish the people who were all working safely at the time of the incident. They hold all-hands meetings, roll out re-training, hold safety awareness workshops. The intention of the leader is to demonstrate they want to take safety seriously and act straight away. The fear that a future incident occurs and the leader was not perceived to have done anything the last time may be present. The unintended message, however, is that the leaders have blamed the worker.

6.1 Typical Leader Tours

Acting straight away is a classic rationalisation; it's a reaction that provides relief to the leaders and managers in the aftermath of the injury: "I went to see Joe in hospital, therefore this proves I care about him." It could be sincere, it could be politics. I prefer to hear leaders say things like, "I don't care how much it costs but we must create a safe place for our people to work." Without detailed knowledge of the contributory factors that led to the injury, most of the knee-jerk leadership reactions are not making the future safer. These actions are more likely making the post-injury period very frustrating for those people who work safely all the time. This can therefore be distracting and dangerous for the rest of the organisation.

Similarly, some leaders who wish to publicly demonstrate their commitment to safety conduct directors' safety tours. Indeed, the Institute of Directors here in the UK suggested that board members should be regularly seen on the shop floor (from their guidance document, 'Leading health and safety at work').

It is important to consider what is expected to happen as a result of a director's visit to a workplace. Is overall safety likely to improve because a leader has shown workers that it is important enough to the director to devote his or her time to? Or is it to enable the director to keep in touch with what is going on? Do such visits really add value, and what actually happens as a result of a workplace visit? In some companies the director is set a target for the number of tours they have to do per year, and it is common for those targets to be attached to financial incentives.

It's important to note that the director's visit will be relevant at the time of the visit. It will elicit a response - perhaps get a site manager or supervisor thinking about a few things - but the director will be gone after a few hours, and most probably won't return for at least a month, perhaps longer. Both the director and the site leader most probably have the best of intentions. The director genuinely intends to demonstrate a commitment to safety. The site manager genuinely wants to act on the director's comments. However, a director can't simply walk around a site and make some comments (insightful or not) and then just expect things to improve.

The behaviours a director sees during a tour are the results of the temporary environment they themselves have created simply by being present, and so workforce behaviours on the day are a reflection of this temporary environment. The everyday environment will return when the visit is over. Directors' visits are not a way for creating sustainable behaviour change. Everyday site environments are the result of the decisions that directors have made regarding their sites over the last few months and years. Until the director works to change the everyday environment so that it can support long term behavioural change, all they have are good intentions in a vacuum.

It is possible that a director's tour can be a value-adding activity but, unless this is measured, the value of the visit is a matter of faith. It is also rare for directors to consider that they may be reducing safety on site by visiting, and taking the time to consider what they might say or do that will avoid that outcome.

6.2 Valuable Leader Tours

A tour that is both productive and enlightening might look a little like this:

- The director speaks to the site manager directly and asks if it's OK to visit the site, and when it would be convenient.
- There is no entourage; the director turns up in mufti rather than Armani, and meets and talks with the site manager.
- The director gets an appropriate site induction and walks around site looking for positive things to comment on, while keeping an eye out for things they can learn.
- The director does not criticise anything, but asks questions about the site, the people, the suppliers, subcontractors, asking anything as long as no advice or aversive comments escape.
- They ask the site manager what they think can be improved upon, what could be better, where the team are focusing their efforts etc.
- The director resists any temptation to solve any problems.

The purpose of the visit is to see what the site is really like; to witness it as real and as unpolished as is possible. To silently and discreetly observe the evidence that indicates what kind of environment has been created by the company. This takes great discipline. It's worth considering how directors are coached, and if someone can accompany them on visits to give them feedback on the behaviours they exhibit during the visit.

What happens after the visit - how the director uses the information they have gathered - is more critical and beneficial than the visit itself. Anyone in a position of authority who can't stay quiet when observing the environment that they have created should avoid visiting the workplace. Their comments will simply drive aversive behaviours and make the site less safe overall.

6.3 Employee Reward Schemes

Another well-intentioned common practice that generally drives aversive behaviours are employee reward schemes. Good leadership needs no contrived alternatives; most people don't have a 'child of the month award' at home. People care for their children and create a safe, happy home; they don't do it with initiatives and signs on the walls. People want to be treated with respect, and anything cheesy at work will likely be lampooned by the majority (albeit in private). A lot of cynicism from workers and managers is driven by these schemes that have good intentions but are simply a substitute for good leadership.

Some employee of the month schemes pay out cash bonuses, some award the winner with a car parking space near to the front door. Some schemes build up a financial reward pot for 'no injuries' where all workers get a cash bonus if no injuries are reported. There are many schemes out there which, whilst well intentioned, have the potential to drive the opposite of the intended behaviours whilst simultaneously reducing the integrity of the leadership team.

6.4 Near Misses And Close Calls

The reporting of injuries is important for learning safety lessons, record-keeping and of course is ethically the right thing to do. The reporting of close calls (sometimes known as near misses) is often assumed to be important for injury prevention. This assumption has recently been analysed more closely and found to be dubious. The link between close calls and injuries/fatalities was made by Heinrich

in his famous triangle and its variants through the years. It appears to
show that by reducing close calls, it is possible to reduce injuries and
fatalities. This is the foundation on which many safety policies are
built, and research has now shown it to be flawed. Reducing near
misses will not reduce injuries or fatalities. (For further reading, see
Behavioural Science Technology, White Paper, New Findings on
Serious Injuries and Fatalities, 2011.)

On face value it feels right that information from an increasing
number of close call reports would result in a safer workplace. The
more information there is regarding what might go wrong, the more
opportunities there are to prevent those things. Of course it is vital to
know about injuries and about important close calls, but asking for
every single thing to be reported and logged is often counterproductive from a behavioural point of view.

Close call cards and formal observations will not necessarily promote
safe behaviours. Of course, close call reporting and observation cards
do not inherently make workplaces unsafe but they can introduce
distractions. It is therefore important to find an appropriate
compromise and agree a level of reporting with the workers. Perhaps
look to the home: What do we do with our children to keep them
safe? Near-miss reporting cards are not a feature of most families.
Virtual safety paperwork and processes distract supervisors from
actually supervising, whereas parents have fewer externally-imposed
barriers to creating a safe place for their children. What is needed to
improve safety in both work and home is people speaking with one
another, and developing strong, caring relationships.

An organisational culture where serious conversations regarding safe
working regularly occur will increase safe performance. It is both
possible and essential for leaders to create an environment where one
worker looks out for another, where a worker wants and expects
challenge if they are doing something that puts themselves and others
at risk. It does take a lot of determined leadership effort, but the
leadership behaviours required to achieve it are relatively simple if the
leader has a good understanding of the impact of their own behaviour

on the workplace environment. A good place to begin is for leaders to frequently ask for dissenting opinions and to enthusiastically welcome any challenges to their own behaviours and choices.

It's important to realise that making workers report things that they consider are unnecessary - such as reporting every bump and scrape, or policing people holding the handrail on the stairs in the office - is inadvertently trivialising safety. Safety policies tend to put equal emphasis on all the rules rather than emphasising the activities that actually make a difference to the worker, like completing tasks safely. Leaders should be wary of functionaries choosing easy-to-police processes that could inadvertently make the workplace less safe.

6.5 Target Zero

Target zero is a simple aspirational target. It sends a seemingly uncomplicated message to the workforce. However, it has undoubtedly made a number of workplaces less safe. For some, safety has inadvertently become a numbers game that has little to do with really keeping people safe. All leaders want their workplaces to be injury-free. Publicly stating this aspiration therefore seems to be perfectly safe, and desirable. It's the truth, and leaders want to demonstrate their aspiration of having everyone go home unhurt every day. It can be difficult to accept that saying something that is genuinely desired will cause problems.

The first problem with zero targets is that all anyone can ever do is fail. A continual threat of failure makes it less likely that desired behaviours can develop and be maintained over time. Discretionary effort requires the potential for positive reinforcement, and this cannot be developed in an aversive environment. Another side effect is that if someone is injured, the vast majority of workers are inadvertently punished, as they are told that they have failed to achieve a target that was outside their personal control.

Zero injury policies often drive out honest reporting and this means that important lessons don't get learned. Information on injuries and incidents is necessary in order to create safe places for people to work.

Asking for injuries to be reported whilst at the same time demanding that there are to be no injuries at all creates a paradox. People must choose which directive is more important. It is impossible to satisfy both demands. Zero injuries is not reasonably practicable. It is also statistically non-viable. Of course it is desirable, but making it a target is counterproductive. Back to the family - do you have a zero injury target at home? What? You don't care about your family's safety?

'Zero' measures also tend to generate undesirable over-reactions from senior leaders when things go wrong, making workplaces less safe. Zero measures do not allow for different maturities of safety standards. The policy is designed and adopted with the best of intentions by most leaders. However the primary impact is that unsafe behaviours are blamed on the workers rather than the leaders who created the working environment. Blaming workers is a slippery slope; only a bad worker blames his tools!

6.6 Personal Responsibility

Some safety campaigns encourage the 'at risk' worker to fix something that is unsafe if they see or feel it. Campaigns like this have little impact on the worker in that crucial moment regarding the next safe or unsafe behaviour. It is a flawed strategy to solely rely on an individual worker to stop work if they see or feel that something is unsafe. It is also presumptive to assume that all workers know there is something wrong, especially ones that are new to the organisation/project.

It is possible for an individual to see something 'unsafe' and still carry on with the task at hand. Frequently, this is because of the balance of immediate consequences. When finishing a task, the consequences to the performer always favour completing the task rather than stopping. In other words, it is usually not immediately reinforcing to stop work. Additionally the 'rare event trap' argues that an incident or injury will not occur anyway. The balance of consequences will most often support the continuation of whatever is being done at the time.

So, if a leader wants their workforce to 'be safe' or 'don't walk by' if they see something unsafe, they have to make sure that the workers find it more reinforcing to do so than to carry on with their task. Safety has to become part of the overall task itself, and this is the responsibility of the leaders, not the workers. Every behaviour needs an antecedent and a reinforcing consequence for it to occur. The behaviour of 'stopping the task at hand and carrying out a corrective action' needs both an antecedent and a sufficiently supporting consequence.

In theory, there should be plenty of antecedents around the performer to prompt the behaviour. The performer may see a barrier that has blown down, a cable lying across a path or a dangerous waste material that should be picked up. However, if observations show that these undesired situations are not being fixed by the 'at risk' worker, we can assume that, although the antecedents exist, they are not yet paired with sufficiently reinforcing consequences.

The concept of stimulus control can help here. It is probable that the worker can be encouraged to respond favourably to a risk that is present in the work environment but has been historically disregarded. This is achieved by introducing a new stimulus and pairing it with the risky situation. If, for example, the worker's supervisor consistently prompts the stoppage of a task or activity during a risky situation, the worker will eventually be conditioned to respond the same way to any risky situation without the supervisor present. The risky situation now has stimulus control in the place of the supervisor. The supervisor doesn't have to police safety. The supervisor does, however, need to praise the right thing when they see it (and so must all the leaders in the organisational chain).

Using this technique, it is possible for the supervisor to 'condition' the at-risk worker to respond in the desired way. How long this takes depends upon each performer and the consistency and frequency of the supervisor's actions. The more consistent and frequent the stimulus from the supervisor, the quicker the conditioning will be. This is how leaders create the environment they want, or get the environment they deserve. Leaders can easily maintain high-performing teams using simple and frequent attention coupled with skilful feedback.

6.7 Intended vs. Actual Integrity

Wherever there is any gap between what a leader says and what they do, then uncertainty and inconsistency emerges from the people around them. It is straightforward to observe, and most noticeable in a number of everyday behaviours where people say one thing but something else happens: People say they will call someone back but they don't; they say they will turn up on time to a meeting and then don't; they agree to an action and don't complete it on time; they say that they will order the equipment but don't; they say that they have allowed the worker enough time but they haven't; they say they want feedback, but punish it when it happens.

It is possible for leaders and supervisors to create the environment where they do what they say. It is possible to call someone back; it is possible to agree to an action and complete it. It is possible to create an environment where the leaders throughout an organisation coach one another, get used to being challenged and to challenging one another. Ultimately, this creates an environment where supervisors coach their workers to look out for each other. Keeping people safe is about talking every day and creating the environment where keeping each other safe is the norm. It is possible for supervisors to have daily conversations with workers and ask them what went well, what didn't, what needs to be done differently. Arguably, having these conversations, responding well, and acting on the outcomes is the only blanket policy an organisation needs.

This will happen if the leaders create the right conditions for themselves so they can do what they say they are going to do, consistently, at every level in the organisation. The best way to test if this is happening is to get a frequent and accurate read on the workplace environments via feedback surveys (see chapter 9).

6.8 Bottom Up Or Top Down?

Another popular myth is the idea that a culture can be led from the bottom up rather than top down. Scientifically, the fundamental truth is that workplace environments are created, maintained and adjusted by leaders, top down. The idea that any workforce is able to set a workplace culture that is not in line with its leadership is simply inaccurate in most organisations.

The safety arena is peppered with non-scientific initiatives. Real safety requires leaders to continuously look for what's actually working and watch for and remove any distracting bureaucratic 'initiatives' that may have crept into their organisation.

Part II
7. Next Steps

7.1 Strategic, Scientific Leadership

A leader has to deliberately create safe workplace environments. A safe workplace cannot be created by a contract, work procedures, rules or the law. Nor can it be achieved solely via simple processes such as start of shift briefings, tool box talks, safety stand downs etc. These activities can set general expectations, but will only be useful if managed with an understanding of the unintended impact they may have. The safe (or unsafe) working environment is created and maintained by the leaders of all the people within the workplace environment.

At the BMT Leadership conference in May 2014, then Director of Capital Delivery at National Grid, Ian Galloway OBE said, "You cannot manage safety, but you can create the conditions for safe performance to occur." Safety is a by-product of all the tasks being undertaken in an organisational workplace. Safety, quality, production, operations, commissioning, etc. are all outputs, and the by-products of doing work.

At the BMT Leadership conference in May 2016, ex-Supreme Commander of NATO General Jack Sheehan said, "Leaders create the conditions for success." Many leaders do not realise how much what they 'say and do' affects the people within their workplaces. Positive or destructive throwaway comments by leaders can impact the working conditions for many workers and for long periods of time thereafter. A leader who reacts emotionally when something goes wrong will be the last person to apologise and the last person to realise that whatever safety issue occurred, it did so in an environment that they created, that they maintained, and for which they are still responsible.

A large number of leaders have been presiding over safe businesses for many years. They make safety a personal quest and deliver artful leadership with skill. They do not rely on procedures and processes. They have those things, but don't rely on them. One of those leaders, Alasdair Cathcart, Senior Vice President at the Bechtel Corporation, said "Safety is a leadership responsibility. It is the barometer of everything else that goes on in our projects." Leaders like Alasdair always have a simply articulated strategy regarding leadership. Messages regarding their expectations are repeated often and they never miss an opportunity to demonstrate great leadership. Martin Lundstedt, the CEO of Volvo Group, recently said, "There are two kind of farmers: One goes out every morning and counts the golden eggs, demanding more from the hen. The other looks after the hen."

Successful strategies focus on what is needed to deliver the organisation's products or services successfully, efficiently and without putting anyone at risk. The starting point is defining success for the organisational entity. What does success look like as an output, and what are all the things that need to be done to ensure that success is achieved? The most successful safety strategies are not really about safety specifically, and this is because real safety in the workplace is a by-product of all the daily behaviours occurring in the workplace environments.

A successful safety strategy is notable for its simplicity. It sets the tone, it describes what success looks like, it proffers simple measures that everyone agrees will produce a fair report card on the success of the strategy. The best strategies describe how to create and maintain the environment for success, from an executive perspective. They detail what the leaders are going to do and spell out what they expect from everyone else.

7.2 Strategic Safety Plan

The process of creating the strategy is a journey of discovery. It is a chance to build robust relationships through the identification of problems and their solutions, leading to a shared goal. Before commencing this journey, it is worth spending a few moments pondering the following:

- Why does the organisation need a safety strategy?
- What do the leaders in the organisation want to happen as a result of creating this strategy?
- Are the right people in charge of this exercise?
- Who will it affect?
- Who needs to support it?
- What does success look like in the organisation: Day-to-day success as well as long-term success.
- What do the actual day-to-day norms look like today, and how close is the organisation to achieving day-to-day success right now?
- How will this strategy help to create the desired environment where day-to-day success will happen?
- What has to change right at the top of the organisation for this to be able to become a success?
- Is this exercise being undertaken for the right ethical reasons?
- How quickly do you want change to occur?

Change for the better does not have to be disruptive or all-encompassing. The most sustainable change programmes are the ones that move the pieces one step at a time in a logical and well-planned manner. Most problems in organisations comprise a lot of dysfunctions that are usually simple and obvious to uncover. They may have developed over a number of years, but they are still usually relatively easy to fix. It's normally fairly easy to discover dysfunction by asking the people in the business, "If you could wave a magic wand and fix something here, what would it be?" Office workers (who often create the site working conditions) usually wish for fewer emails, better and shorter meetings, better car parking, or for someone to stop doing something or start doing something. These things are not fundamentally difficult to fix: They are all the outputs of humans behaving.

A behaviour stops when it is punished and a behaviour is maintained or increases when in receipt of reinforcement. This basic scientific formula works every time. Successful behavioural change is brought about by analysing the workplace environment and adjusting it such that the desired behaviours occur regularly. This is achieved by spreading an understanding of behavioural science sufficiently to get a tipping point of knowledge within the environment in question. It's not complex; it does, however, take effort for enough of the individuals to learn and practise the new skills.

The best leaders put most of their execution efforts into creating an environment that supports what they want to get done. Creating the right environment means that the leader focuses some effort and experimentation into which of their own behaviours they might change. Perhaps re-arranging their regular schedule, engaging their direct reports to help, changing their physical environment, or spending time at home within the week to do their thinking and also to 'get out of the way'. There are products now on the market that electronically give feedback on behaviours. Fitness trackers are commonplace, for example. Microsoft's Delve Analytics provides an interesting tool to help people understand how they are actually spending their time. Feedback received from a neutral source like a machine has the advantage of not carrying any emotion; the feedback is simply data, nothing more.

Making small changes in one's schedule may feel like setting too low a goal, especially when the overall aim is sweeping cultural change. Setting one's sights low in the beginning does not mean that you are settling for less. The leader has to be persuaded that they can change, and this early phase is designed to do just that. It also means that a solid foundation is being built from which higher goals can be reached. Only once that foundation has been laid is it possible to work on anything more complex. When these underlying personal issues have been resolved, it becomes possible to focus on continuous improvement across other areas of the business.

7.3 The Self-Weeding Garden

Continuous improvement is not a natural process. The self-weeding garden does not exist; in fact the opposite is true if considering systems and processes. In a number of common situations, nature does us no favours. We do not naturally continually improve, we do not naturally get healthier, we do not naturally become experts in our field. These things take effort, they take deliberate practice. Success always follows a specific plan and deliberate effort.

Like the garden, the easiest strategy for continual improvement is to keep a focus on maintenance. If the workplace environment is continually maintained then that environment will produce the behaviours that will deliver the needs of the organisation, and deliver them safely. It's important for leaders to be continually seeking out areas that are not quite right and adjusting them. The first step in this process is to realise that this won't happen naturally. As General Jack Sheehan frequently says, "If you stand still, you're dead."

7.4 The High-Performing Team

All high-performing teams exist in an environment where a few specific, critical daily behaviours are able to occur. To purposefully design such an environment, it is vital to be able to articulate what those daily behaviours are. The team must also ensure there are no barriers to high performance. The beneficial and efficient use of time is always key, as is an abundance of feedback. Learning the skills to effectively deliver and receive feedback takes time and practise.

A high-performing team is a much aspired-to but rarely seen entity. Our surveys over the last fourteen years have led to the conclusion that the genuine high-performing team is rare. The most common type of high-performing teams are usually small, on a specific job task or project, have a talented leader who is happy leading, and have very specific time-bound objectives.

It appears that most teams are thrown together because of who's available rather than who is needed. Some leaders take their old team with them to the next job and create the instant, already fully tested, new team. The really good leaders don't take anyone with them; they set out to create the next great team. They know what is needed and they know how to achieve it.

As with a sound safety strategy, it is important to articulate what success looks like when looking for high-performance. Here are some characteristics that might be found in the workings of a high-performing team:

- They measure a small number, and an equal balance, of lead and lagging measures.
- They have 'frequent and short' team briefs.
- All meetings take less than one hour and aim to involve fewer than 7 people.
- They measure and cost out meetings and publish that data regularly - to avoid 'meeting creep'.
- They rarely have more than two layers of hierarchy in operational meetings.
- They have a goal for a reduction of paperwork over time.
- The leaders are collegial when they need to be and, when necessary, they lead.
- The leaders react in a deliberate and measured way when things go wrong and don't create worse conditions for the future.
- The leaders are the least busy people; they are always available (or very close to being).
- Everyone is focused on the task; no-one is attempting to spice up the day with mischief.
- High-performing teams can initially appear comparatively boring next to the last-minute firefighting teams.
- The necessary workplace activities that create aversion are managed well.
- People are able to do their job properly, they have that strong feeling of belonging.
- People are successful, they advance into more and more interesting career scenarios.
- Everyone mostly feels positive about being at work.

8. The Future - BMT For Safety

Behavioural Management Techniques (BMT) is a blend of behavioural science tools and project management skills. My call to action is to take safety to its next evolutionary phase: A fully scientific approach to safety based on BMT. Knowledge of behavioural science can produce efficient and safe ways of working, operating, managing and leading. Combined with basic project management skills, the likelihood of sustaining those things over time is greatly increased.

The BMT approach to safety is characterised by the following key elements:

- The focus is first on leaders, who then focus on their staff/workers.
- The leadership team learn behavioural science to a basic level of competence.
- Prior to introducing new initiatives, the current workplace environments are surveyed and analysed.
- There is a strong emphasis on feedback and developing trusting relationships.
- Leaders aim to achieve high engagement, and encourage the use of recognition and reinforcement, positive reinforcement in particular.
- It is a flexible approach that provides a set of skills and a knowledge base that is applicable anywhere in the business, not just safety.
- Leaders are coached to use data in a way that always has a positive impact.
- It encourages a balanced approach that gets to the contributory factors of any problems.
- The workforce consistently indicate in surveys that safety is more important than production.

8.1 How To Get People To Consistently Do The Right Thing

Achieving strategic outcomes, building high-performing teams and delivering quality products and services safely all depend on the leader developing a strategy, and designing and delivering the conditions for high levels of performance to occur. This chapter will outline a framework to help the leader understand why they are getting current results, and how to approach changes to improve performance.

8.2 The Performance Equation

The performance equation was published in *The Too Busy Trap (2nd edition)*. This section is taken from that book.

Dr Ryan Olson is a leading behavioural research scientist at Oregon Health and Science University. He designed the performance equation, which is:

Performance = (Motivation + Ability) - Obstacles
Where:
Performance is the delivery of a valuable result via human behaviour.

Motivation is linked to receiving recognition for a job well done and receiving regular feedback on performance. At work, someone's motivation will normally come from natural positive consequences in the task, their peers or their supervisor/manager. Motivation tends to be higher when people feel confident, free, and valued. People's past experiences affect their motivation (e.g., their own unique reinforcers), however the local workplace environment will be the primary source of motivation at any given time. Task completion can be motivating, especially when people have a good fit with their task assignments, but not always. Great leaders purposefully 'supply' motivation into the environment where it may not otherwise naturally occur.

Ability is the ability to do the job required. Does the performer have the necessary knowledge and skill level required to do his or her daily tasks? The first step to ensuring ability is selecting people with the right experience and skills for the job. However, after that they will require the right training, information and knowledge. Job ability requirements also change over time, so it is important to ensure that people get ongoing support and coaching. A person's ability also depends on the right people around them being available when they need them and enough time being allocated for each task.

Obstacles or 'the removal of obstacles' involves making sure that people can do their job well, and that their environment is free from safety and health hazards, unnecessary complications, rules or bureaucracy. Work procedures and processes should be lean and straightforward. Communication, including emails and meetings, must be uncomplicated and effective. If there are barriers preventing people from completing simple tasks quickly and easily then high performance is just not possible. High levels of performance occur when frustrations and distractions are low and where people can consistently do what they say they will do.

Performance = (Motivation + Ability) - Obstacles

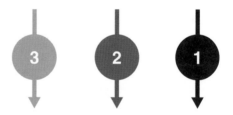

Dr Olson states that the first step (and highest priority) in a performance analysis process is to look at the obstacles that stymie current performance. The second place to focus is the ability of the performers, including the leaders that are presiding over the particular workplace environment. Step three is to look at motivation. It's quite common that once obstacles have been removed and the performer has acquired the necessary skills and time to complete the task, motivation fixes itself. This is because steps one and two were usually the key elements stopping the performer all along.

Understanding the workplace environment of the performer is paramount in using scientific methods to adapt behaviour. All three components in the performance equation should be analysed from the performer's perspective. Simply put, if the performance isn't occurring then it's because the performer either can't or won't carry out the desired behaviours. This is illustrated below:

Performance = (Motivation + Ability) - Obstacles

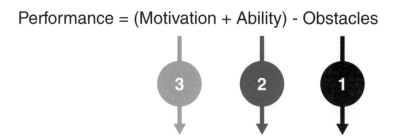

Olson's simple process can be combined with behavioural analysis to change the environment where the performer can achieve their goals as illustrated below:

Performance = (Motivation + Ability) - Obstacles

8.3 Obstacles To Safety Performance

Where barriers to performance exist, no matter how skilled and motivated a person is to succeed, they simply cannot do so. It is therefore vital to identify and remove barriers to performance. Common obstacles include a lack of sufficient time, tools and equipment to do a job. Not only are these things obstacles themselves, but they also constitute a distraction - and people who are focused on anything other than their current task cannot perform at their best, or as safely as they might.

Common distractions for staff include poor IT systems, annoying bosses, rules felt to be unnecessary (lids on coffee cups, reverse car parking etc.), stress caused by feeling too busy, feelings of being undervalued etc. It is possible to predict many of these and for leaders to ensure that the people have minimal distractions. Some leaders suggest that their workforce should simply 'get over' minor distractions and focus on their work; a 'just do it' policy. This places the responsibility for working safely directly onto the workforce, regardless of the conditions. If workers find themselves in a dysfunctional environment they will understandably feel they have little choice but to accept the situation or leave.

Some barriers to high levels of safety performance are deeply ingrained in the organisational culture. Mature organisations have a strong collection of behavioural patterns that have been shaped over time. Each organisation's current workplace environment supports all the day-to-day behaviours, both functional and dysfunctional, maintaining them over time. This is known as 'institutional repertoire'.

Institutional repertoire produces the illusion of permanence, the personal repertoires of the individuals in the organisation following the 'unwritten' rules of their local environment. Everyone complies with behavioural norms that have developed over time. In the moment, people shy away from telling the truth about what they see and hear. It is a way of working that makes the daily lives of the performers an 'acceptable' compromise, with the underlying dysfunctions still present.

Institutional repertoires are primary blockers to change; repertoires have a strong inertia. Breaking out of a dysfunctional scenario requires an intervention of some kind, which will in turn require a sense of urgency. It takes considerable planning and effort to create sustainable change. It takes effort to follow a diet and eat the right food, it takes effort to exercise, and it takes effort to be a great leader. It takes time and effort to do most tangible worthwhile things in a sustainable way.

Thankfully, time and effort that is well-directed can be naturally reinforcing for the person making the changes. The main ingredients are leadership and a simple delivery strategy. People are always happy to devote time and effort to a great person with a great plan, who is clearly trying to make it as easy as possible for everyone to simply do their jobs safely.

Harvard Business School Professor John Kotter laid out a plan regarding change management. It starts with 'first create a sense of urgency'. It moves on to 'form a guiding coalition' but as Kotter points out himself, not many people get past 'create a sense of urgency', such is the power and fluency of the day-to-day behaviours that form the institutional repertoire. All the great organisations and great people have a strong repertoire; the key is to be able to create a shaping plan (see chapter 8.6) that takes it to a better, more effective, safer place.

8.4 Ability And Motivation

Once most of the obstacles have been removed, Performance (according to the performance equation) will be determined by someone's ability to do a task and by the amount of motivation they have to carry out the task. Ability (competence) to do a task either exists or it doesn't in the individual. Motivation will change over time depending on local environmental conditions. For a leader to ensure that everyone can perform well, they must understand the power and the responsibility they have to provide motivation through the creation of a positive workplace environment.

Some employers believe that 'getting paid' (or worse, 'not getting fired') should be motivation enough at work. This is simply untrue, behaviourally speaking. In an ideal workplace, workers display 'discretionary effort' much of the time. When operating under discretionary effort, people deliver multiples of production over and above the minimum required. The minimum is defined by the level of effort required to avoid punishment. Discretionary effort occurs when performers can deliver work because they want to (under positive reinforcement) rather than because they have to (under negative reinforcement). The difference is crucial, especially with safety.

Specific safety-related behaviours rarely naturally deliver positive reinforcement for the performer. Even when someone wants to be safe, and are happy about the fact that they are (for example) wearing all the correct PPE for a task, the behaviour is ultimately driven by the performer's wish to avoid a potential injury, and not by their intrinsic enjoyment of wearing bright orange clothes.

If most safety-related behaviours are driven by a wish to avoid a threat, but a leader wants to get discretionary effort from their people, then a solution is required. The answer is embedded in robust relationships. This does not mean that the leader must get to know all their workforce in detail. Instead, it means that the leader should understand the power of relationships and harness that power by building a coaching culture.

The most powerful drivers of behaviours in a local environment are delivered by 'consequence providers'. These people are usually a performer's immediate supervisor (or at home, the parent of a child or one's partner). The consequence provider is the person most able to motivate the performer to complete a task. They are also the person most able to demotivate a performer. The behaviours of a consequence provider have a massive influence on the behaviours of the performer and so on up the consequence chain.

In a typical medium-sized organisation, the worker at the coal face is most influenced by their immediate supervisor, who is most influenced by their manager, who is most influenced by their senior leader, who is most influenced by their Director, who is most influenced by the CEO. Thus, the CEO's behaviours will affect the behaviours of the worker at the coal face, albeit with a time delay. The responsibility of everyone in this long consequence chain should be to ensure that their behaviours ultimately have the desired impact on the worker delivering the work. This is the primary responsibility of the leader.

Some workplaces have in-house personnel and sub-contracted people within the same environment. The leadership responsibility when deciding to bring in 'outsiders' now extends to working out how these distinct groups will work harmoniously together. They need to work out how everyone involved will engender a sense of looking after each other. This 'harmony' strategy is often forgotten when decisions to subcontract are made in the boardroom. Executives often see the obvious financial benefits but do not carry out the behavioural sense-check that would reveal the potential downsides.

The best examples of good leadership show leaders observing from afar, gently tweaking things in a timely fashion whilst trying not to overtly interfere. The best leadership is not being prescriptive about the 'how' but taking advantage of the abundant opportunities to enquire, recognise and reinforce, understanding that real sustainable power lies in coaching confidently, but gently and over time. When coaching, leaders might have a dialogue about required results (rather than imposing them), ask questions to find out how the person they are coaching plans to achieve them, and discover any worries or concerns the coachee has about making that happen. It is worth taking the time to coach well: After all, these are the people that create the wealth for the business, literally and figuratively.

Some knowledge workers encounter difficulties with relationship-building. It is common for highly technically-qualified people to be also under-qualified in leadership skills. They sometimes display a temptation to assume that 'we know best' and this leads to a discomfort when delegating tasks to others, no matter how competent the recipient.

It's worth respecting the fact that the best person to comment on the tasks ahead and how they should be completed are the performers themselves. A shift of focus from managing workers to supporting them is a key tenet of sustainable safe working practices. Understanding that, and taking every step to make it as easy as possible for workers to do their work safely, is where sustainable safe business delivery occurs reliably. For work tasks that will be repeated over long periods of time, a procedure can be agreed with the performers. Leaders can provide all the right tools, technology and training to complete the tasks safely. Negotiation over time periods for task completion also need to be agreed. For bespoke work tasks, a slightly different process is required, following the principle of the same 'achieved by agreement' process above.

For this way of working to succeed, everyone needs strong communication skills. The ability to deliver artful feedback and receive it well rarely comes naturally. It is a learned skill and a necessary one for building a coaching culture.

8.5 Feedback

Feedback is defined as 'information about past performance that helps improve future performance'. Without feedback, no-one can get better at any task they do. Some feedback occurs naturally in the environment, but verbal feedback must be sought for and nurtured. The amount of verbal feedback in an environment is a good barometer of how effective the base culture is. High-performing teams score very highly when asked about levels of feedback within the team. Where people regularly talk and exchange information about work and about personal performance, everyone's performance improves quickly.

Timing is crucial with feedback. If someone delivers excellent feedback, but long after the behaviour occurred, it is likely to have a weak effect (it may also annoy the recipient). This is sometimes the case with annual reviews. Becoming skilled at delivering and receiving timely feedback requires an understanding of the downstream impact of one's own behaviours, and also requires practice. Coaching helps build up skills in the successful delivery of effective feedback.

Relationships affect the success of feedback being received as it was intended. Strong relationships, where people care about and respect one another, can be rich in positive and constructive feedback. Both parties understand that the feedback is a genuine attempt to help improve performance. One of the best ways to improve relationships is to consistently ask for feedback and act upon it. The recipient can then react well to it, and over time a trusting relationship will develop.

Understanding more about behavioural pinpointing (breaking down subjective terms like 'efficient' or 'high-performing' into their many constituent objective, measurable behaviours) will helps improve feedback loops. Building a coaching culture - where people discuss personal development and leadership skills, as opposed to tasks and operational coaching - will be beneficial for everyone. One of the best ways to evaluate one's own knowledge and understanding is to teach others. A coaching culture helps everyone to improve their own performance.

When offering feedback to others, it is important to be aware of the recipient's environment. If the relationship between the person delivering feedback and the recipient is anything other than positive, it is likely that any feedback will be seen as criticism and often disregarded. If the timing is wrong when feedback is offered, and the recipient is not ready to hear it, again it will been seen as criticism. The golden combination with feedback is to deliver it in a positive environment and with thoughtful timing.

When giving others feedback, consider these factors:

- How robust is this relationship?
- Make feedback data-based, not just opinion - this helps to ensure the feedback is not related to emotions.
- Describe pinpointed behaviours for feedback.
- Ensure the timing of feedback is sensitive and the timeframe useful.
- All feedback should be in the best interests of the recipient.

When asking for feedback:

- Be specific about what you want.
- Say "thank you" whatever the person says.
- Ask people to be specific in their feedback.
- Ask, "How do I make/do something better?"

The 4:1 ratio is often cited when referring to feedback. It illustrates that people who are good at getting the best out of those around them deliver a minimum of four pieces of positive feedback for every piece of constructive feedback. It is easily misinterpreted, so worth noting that it does not mean looking for one negative piece of feedback for every four positives. Nor does it mean that one has to search out four pieces of positive feedback before any constructive feedback can be given. The ratio is simply an indicator that puts into perspective the way to develop a successful feedback-rich environment: Everyone should be looking out for the 'good things' that are already happening around them, and saying to the people involved that what they have been doing has been noticed and appreciated.

Some safety programmes are based on people giving feedback to the business or to one another. This will work well if feedback is common in all parts of the business, but if no other part of the organisation formally encourages feedback, a disconnect exists. Discussing and sharing opinions on what has been observed feels awkward and contrived if it is only done for one aspect of the business, even when that aspect is safety. It can also feel threatening if the people being observed are only ever the workforce.

When a worker has been observed working unsafely, sometimes the blame is placed on the worker for 'not wanting to work safely'. If the worker has been suitably trained and there are no barriers to their working safely, then considering their motivation is the next step. However, motivation does not only come from within oneself (intrinsic motivation). Generally speaking, extrinsic motivation (feedback supplied by the environment, including other people) is a stronger driver of behaviour. Therefore, leaders must ensure that sufficient feedback for both desired and undesired behaviours is supplied to a worker's environment. Behaviourally speaking, the desired behaviours must be more reinforcing for the worker than the undesired behaviours. When a behaviour has been successfully reinforced, the performer will, in similar circumstances, do more of that behaviour again in the future. Working to improve feedback skills will accelerate this process (see chapter 11 for more on feedback).

8.6 Shaping

Shaping is a behavioural science term that describes working towards a goal by taking a series of small steps over time. If attempts to make changes are not working, then there probably aren't enough shaping steps - the steps are not small and simple enough. Shaping plans are deceptively easy to construct; the biggest difficulty is that people are inclined to make the steps too big. There should be enough small steps so that people read them and think, "This is going to be easy!"

Working without effectively shaped plans might look or feel like:

- Carrying out an expedient solution rather than the correct one.
- Shortening the correct length of time to complete a task to suit the amount of time left in the original plan to complete the task.
- Allowing untested/untrained/inexperienced personnel to carry out the task.
- Use of incorrect materials and/or tools.
- A lack of proper planning.
- Leaders operating a 'management by exception' process, i.e. they are only there when they need you or when something is going wrong.

Working with effectively shaped plans looks and feels like:

- Everyone agrees on the solution and how it is to be achieved at the outset.
- Accurate timescales are applied to each step in the plan, again in agreement with the team.
- All personnel are trained, tested and have a mentor who is looking after their skills development.
- All the right tools are available at the outset of the work.
- The leadership is visible and available.

8.7 Stress Factors

A safety professional responsible for a number of multi-million dollar projects recently noted that: "Stress and frustration factors lead to most of our incidents. I think most management would be surprised at the impact that delay has on people that want to be working and doing a good job. Something as simple as a late delivery will lead to people thinking of an alternative way to do the job or starting a new task, often without discussion or planning."

Uncertainty causes stress. A primary leadership role is to create certainty and by so doing, reduce stress levels for those around them. It is also the leader's job to ensure that people are productive rather than too busy. This distinction is key to developing high levels of performance.

The Yerkes-Dodson stress curve indicates that finding the right amount of stress, or stimulation, is ideal. Stress is not always a bad thing, depending on levels or type of stress experienced. There should be enough so that people are motivated to make changes, but not so much that they have no capacity to do so. This capacity varies from person to person, and is worth considering.

A common cause of 'too busy' induced stressors is the need for people to comply with various processes laid out by a business. Whilst some processes are absolutely necessary, it is often the case that many are a distraction to the real work. Detailed processes have become so normal in many workplaces, especially in the field of safety, that the process itself becomes the work. This may seem desirable, especially when it is felt that following a process will keep people safe, but there is a fundamental flaw in this argument: A process cannot keep a person safe. The workers need the right tools, conditions, time and resources in order to be able to work safely.

8.8 People And Process Considerations

If everyone responded to rules and lists then the simple act of posting a list of chores in the house would result in them being consistently carried out by the teenage children. Writing down how something has to be done is significantly easier to do than working out how to create the environment where it happens reliably. Some things to bear in mind when considering processes include:

- It's very important to have a lean set of work processes for people to follow.
- If processes are sensible and simple, then people will most probably follow them.
- Most workplaces are subjected to some kind of change multiple times every day.
- People can detect subtle changes in their environment; processes can't.
- Processes are designed for ideal workplace conditions, rarely for reality.
- Very often processes are not written by the performer of the process.
- It's very difficult to express the tone of a message on a process.
- Processes rely on people to follow each process to the letter.
- Some business try to hide behind baffling processes rather than focus on effective leadership.
- Successful business and safety is founded in good relationships, not processes.

The antidote to process-overload is to develop annual goals aimed at reducing the number of workplace processes in the organisation. Left to nature, the number of workplace processes will inevitably increase every year through institutional repertoire. A balancing goal will provide an effective counter-weight to this natural phenomenon. Other symptoms of institutional repertoires creeping towards dysfunction include excessive meetings (in terms of length, number, attendees and usefulness) and emails being used where face-to-face communication is possible. Unless purposefully kept in check, these things naturally grow - but they are simple to rectify if a strong leader has the will to do so.

Excessive processes, emails, meetings and other bureaucratic aspects of business eat into the time available to deliver the actual product or service. High performance is only possible when there is sufficient time. Deciding on the daily behaviours required to remove dysfunctional levels of time-consuming tasks will help with this (for example, a team norm may be that there is no cc-ing of emails, or that people communicate face-to-face or by phone, using emails only where other options are not available). The team will need to develop the skills to spot the time-sucking low value tasks and remove or delegate them, and this will require continual reinforcement from the leader.

Fixing these things is not just about reducing the stress caused by feeling too busy, or removing the appearance of being disorganised. It is about the messages that a leader sends to those around them. For example, meetings are opportunities to publicly demonstrate the behaviours that will build trust and strong relationships over time. Keeping meetings short as a rule will make it easier for people to refrain from checking messages or taking calls during them. Attentiveness tells the other meeting attendees that their input is important, sending a strong message that reverberates through the organisation that the leader values the contributions of those around them.

8.9 Deliberate Leadership And Coaching

Sometimes setting a good example isn't enough. There are some leaders that are very good at setting a good example: They brief well, they set clear expectations, they honour their obligations, they preside over short and effective meetings, they manage their email artfully, they set good examples regarding their day-to-day behaviours. Unfortunately simply setting good examples will not mean that direct reports will automatically follow the lead. Sometimes it is still necessary to make sure that nothing goes unsaid in meetings. It may be necessary for the leader to ask the staff if they are setting similar good examples to their own people. I once advised a CEO that she should say to her more interpersonally-challenged direct reports, "For the avoidance of doubt, this was a coaching session."

Coaching relationships can only be successful if the coach and recipient both want to engage in coaching. It's too presumptive to expect that would be possible for a leader and all their direct reports - in fact it encourages everyone to think that coaching is just a process that they 'do', rather than being a permission-based situation where the coach engages the recipient enough that they want to receive coaching.

The Hollin book *Power Coaching* is a good primer for coaching skills and includes a number of coaching suggestions for leaders. I think it's fair to say that a coaching culture is likely to be a productive culture, made up of individual high-performing workplace environments. Generally speaking, there's probably a coaching culture if:

- There are conversations about style, about the way things are said.
- People come to their leaders for advice about dealing with 'people' issues.
- Discussions are Socratic, not just directive.
- Leaders get feedback on their behaviour.
- Leaders know what their team members have concerns about at work, outside of delivery.
- Leaders are able to deliver effective, honest feedback within their team.
- Generally, people respond well to feedback.
- People say things like, "I've been thinking about what you said."
- People feel comfortable apologising.
- People seek feedback and coaching, and not just from their nominated coach.
- People are comfortable asking for clarification: "Just checking…" or "I think you just said…"
- Meetings are effective and actions are completed on time.
- People are confident and comfortable asking for help.
- E-mails are not used for conversations - people mostly talk face-to-face.
- People talk naturally and reassuringly about safety e.g. "Let's talk about how this is going to be done safely."

A leader is obliged to lead everyone in their team, no matter how difficult the relationships. The people who demonstrate they are keen, show they are engaged and respond well to the direction given should also receive coaching, and a work-around should be developed for the others. It can be damaging to force coaching in a relationship where it will not thrive.

9. Measurement

Choosing goals for business is often steeped in all the 'too big' and 'too hard' goals of the past. Most people dive straight into 'what to measure' rather than taking time to examine 'what we are doing now, day-to-day,' and gathering data on the effectiveness of the here and now. In order to do something new, a leader must remove items from their day-to-day behaviours in order to make space for the new things. This is a good time to create a sense of urgency, because most people steadfastly refuse to take anything out of their current daily behaviours without one.

All current behaviours are happening for a reason; they are all subject to a reinforcing and positive present. If they weren't, they would not be happening at all. Changing behaviours can be difficult because, faced with an uncomfortable present in order to get to a positive future, most people opt for the status quo and do not change. All the 'steps before step one' for effective change need to focus on discovering and removing the activities being emotionally embraced right now that don't actually achieve anything. The key to making a better future is first making space for something new.

Creating an environment that supports the behaviours that will deliver success takes a lot of effort and strong relentless leadership. It's not a one-off process; the environment will need to be shaped up and maintained for continued success. Measurement will help direct and maintain a focus on the key components of success.

9.1 Measuring Success

Success is rarely judged on the achievement of 'nothing', yet with traditional health and safety the absence of illness and injuries is commonly the primary measure. Aiming for zero is a difficult quest, as there's nothing to measure apart from failure. Measuring can tell people whether things are getting better. Knowing this means that people can be reinforced for doing the right things. Designing in measures that don't facilitate reinforcement is a poor strategy.

The best leaders design a useful and simple method of measurement for their knowledge workers that operates without frightening them. That's how they create great places to work. The best leaders display confidence, intelligence, humour, and integrity. All the great leaders know what they want and also display a reassuring modicum of self-doubt. The measures these leaders choose are usually a mixture of leading and lagging indicators.

9.2 Leading And Lagging Indicators

Defining a set of effective measures takes trial and error as well as time and effort. Measures have to be specific to the purpose and outputs of the business. It is easier to focus on traditional lagging indicators as these are 'results' and generally easy to collect up and report.

The key to success, however, is knowing what might go wrong before it does and mitigating those things. It is imperative also to know what is going right in an organisation. These two scenarios are where leading indicators are most useful.

A leading indicator is usually a measure of the current behaviours in the environment that will help predict future outcomes. Leading indicators predict the workplace environment. Measuring simple behaviours around 'meetings' or 'communication' will provide data on the likelihood of obligations being honoured. For example, if people turn up to meetings on time and return phone calls when they say they will (leading indicators), these can be a good predictor of survey results that indicate high levels of trust (a lagging result). Measuring this over time will test the cause and effect relationship to establish if there is indeed a correlation.

People find it difficult to attach credence to the value of measuring simple day-to-day leader behaviours. Good leaders breed certainty in the workplace and they can do this simply by honouring their obligations. It can become infectious quite quickly. People like working in workplace environments where there is certainty; staff and manual workers alike.

Most lagging indicators are measures of things that have either already gone right or wrong. Lagging indicators might measure 'a task completed safely' or 'an injury'. Organisations that use positive lagging indicators (such as the number of cables/services *successfully avoided* whilst digging in the road) are utilising measurement in order to contribute to the creation of a positive environment. Testing is crucial for any new measure, and it is always worthwhile asking the people being measured for their opinion on how useful the measure is. There are more examples of leading and lagging indicators in the book *BMT Scorecards*.

9.3 Climate Surveys - Collecting The Intelligence From The Workforce

Many organisations run staff and workforce surveys. Often called climate surveys, these involve gathering feedback from within the organisation to try and understand people's views on the workplace environment. As with most company initiatives, the intentions of these surveys are honourable. With blanket surveys, however, little consideration is taken of the variations in the organisation's often diverse local environments. Surveys can easily become a tick-box exercise for employees and a mandatory exercise for the administrators of the survey. The senior leaders, who genuinely want to understand their organisation better, often end up with skewed responses which only tell them how employees felt at the time they filled out the survey, often some months previously.

A single, long, annual survey will not give leaders the information that they need to adapt the workplace environment. When asking people to complete a survey, there is a temptation to ask all the questions at once. This is justified by the belief that asking people to complete one large survey per year is reasonable. The downside of asking a large number of questions is that people have a limited concentration span. Our surveys suggest that after about 30 questions people stop considering their responses as carefully and begin to answer more quickly and less thoughtfully; they get survey fatigue.

Along with the size, the anonymity of surveys is hugely important. An anonymous survey is much more likely to elicit truthful responses than one where the participant thinks they can be identified. This means that a majority of past survey results could be unreliable. It is common to fail to take into account the power of perception. Surveys should be anonymous, and participants must also believe that they are truly anonymous. For example, employees are often asked to fill in an anonymous survey that begins or ends by asking for the person's department, age range, gender, ethnicity or other details that allows them to be identified. The purpose of these demographic questions is generally innocent and intended to help with analysis, but the outcome is that the survey is no longer perceived to be anonymous. Once that has happened, even once, people no longer believe that surveys are anonymous, and respond accordingly.

Finally, the questions asked in surveys are often presumptive. For example, "I enjoy receiving the company newsletter every month" is a presumptive question. It steers the respondent in the direction that the survey-writer hopes they will respond: We all want our staff to enjoy receiving the newsletter, otherwise we wouldn't take the time to compose and send it. A better question might be, "I always/ sometimes/rarely/never read the newsletter."

A large number of organisational surveys are long winded, peppered with identifiers, claim to be anonymous (but no-one believes it), and laced with presumptive questions. The results can be confusing, voluminous and some make outrageous claims that most people in the organisation instinctively know are not true. It is common for there to be pressure on leaders to improve the survey results compared to last year's - regardless of whether or not the working conditions have improved.

Good leaders run regular, short, anonymous opinion surveys. Every organisational culture can be sampled via small and simple climate surveys. All the very latest information is always available, it simply needs to be mined. Everyone's opinions can be collected and analysed for usefulness and potency. On completion of each survey analysis, the results can be used to steer changes for the better for the wealth-creating performers. It only takes a small group of committed people with some useful data to produce a strategy for the way forward. With leadership support, everyone can act to enrich their workplace.

From a behavioural viewpoint, useful surveys will have a few things in common. They include:

- There are no more than 30 easy-to-answer questions.
- They are repeated within 3 months to periodically gauge progress.
- The results are visible to everyone.
- The results are quickly and visibly acted upon by the organisation's leaders.
- Presumptive questions have been removed or minimised.
- All identifiers have been removed.
- The survey is not delivered online.
- Leaders need to be well prepared to respond well to honest but unfavourable results.

10. Designing A Survey

Here are some notes on designing and executing a successful climate survey. This section includes some things to consider for each stage. There are 3 distinct stages of a successful survey; the pre-survey, the survey itself and then post-survey activities.

10.1 The Purpose Of The Survey

Consider the specific purpose of the survey. It's important to focus on the people most likely to deliver the most useful feedback and information. Leaders may wish to uncover dissenting opinions, collect feedback on recent initiatives, gather an understanding of the safety environment etc. In large organisations choosing a relevant and statistically valid sample of people is key.

10.2 Types Of Survey

The most accurate surveys are anonymous surveys where all the people within the organisation are polled on a selection of pre-tested questions. This is the most expensive and time-consuming survey but delivers by far the best results. Some types of surveys are better than other. The most common surveys include:

- Simple web-based surveys e.g. Survey Monkey. These are usually perceived to be slightly more anonymous than other types. They often have a low return rate, but are usually short. If people are chivvied to complete the online survey, the responses change accordingly.
- Simple paper-based surveys. If these do not require people to fill in identifying details, they are similar in effectiveness to the web-based surveys. If they ask for free-text feedback, people may be rightly wary that their handwriting will be recognisable.
- Complex multi-question web-based surveys. These are rarely anonymous and generally too voluminous to be useful.
- Facilitator-led Q&A sessions with samples of employees. These are not anonymous, but allow the facilitator to examine topics in more depth than other types of survey. They do not offer data to use for future comparison.

- Anonymous voting cards surveys with validation interviews. The surveys are completely anonymous, and the responses are seen 'live' by the people in the room. The interviews enable the topics to be examined in more depth with willing participants.

10.3 Pre-Survey Work

Before a climate survey, useful activities include: Information gathering, desk study, initial interviews, scope setting and agreement of the survey process. The best climate surveys are facilitated by people independent of the organisation. If time and money is available then surveys benefit from initial interviews to narrow the focus to the 'right questions'. Any interviews must be carried out by someone who is affable and non-threatening. A pilot survey on one or two representative groups then takes place, the data is analysed and the information used to refine the questions for the final survey.

10.4 Developing Survey Questions

Here are some tips for developing useful survey questions:

- Ask easy-to-understand, short and simple questions. Provide answer sets that cover every eventuality. Only use acronyms to shorten questions if everyone will understand them.
- If the question is 'absolute' one way or the other ('this is very good' or 'this is very bad') it makes analysis easy.
- Aim for a maximum of 30 questions per survey: Research says that once people have answered 25-30 questions they begin to fatigue.
- Consider using a mixture of open questions (for framing) and closed statements (for narrowing the focus). Design and test where they come in the order of the survey.
- Don't use aspirational questions or answer sets. Leaders sometimes want to ask questions in surveys that support what they believe to be true. Avoid asking a wishful statement. Aspiration flows both ways so if people are asked if they agree with the statement "We take safety seriously here" the answer is mostly going to be "Yes."

- Avoid asking two questions in one. Questions that ask about more than one topic will never elicit a useable answer. The person answering the question may be confused by the question. If they do respond, they will just focus on the aspect most relevant to them and the analyst will not know what that was.

- Be aware that 'I' statements are more favourably answered. 'I' statements are answered in a more aspirational way, so balance them with 'we' and 'people' statements and questions about others. This allows survey analysts to factor in the ratio of 'me to others' bias.

- Look for a contrast between answers to questions. Watch out for contrasts or contradictions between answers. This allows a survey analyst to follow up in more detail and narrow the focus of the question next time round.

- Asking for opinion vs. asking for speculation. Facts are preferable, but opinions are the next best thing. Opinions are formed on what people hear and see. Asking people to answer speculatively is really just asking people to guess their answer. Avoid this by pre-testing the questions. Consider if the people being surveyed actually have enough knowledge on this subject, or if they will have to speculate.

- Be wary of presumptive questions. An example of a presumptive question is "When did you stop caring about your appearance?" This kind of question is impossible to answer. Care must be taken not to allow prejudices or assumptions to be baked into the questions. Ask someone who is not part of the survey group if they think any of the questions are presumptive.

- Watch for questions that will trigger a positive bias. If the current workplace environment doesn't reflect an overtly open and honest culture, the respondents may prefer not to admit that something is wrong. They will likely answer questions in a way that shuts down any perception of threat. Asking the same question from each end of two extremes of perspective will identify this as a potential problem, e.g. 'Our workplace is safe' and 'Our workplace is dangerous'. Answering contrary to the norm will be more difficult for people due to natural biases.

- Don't waste questions. Never ask a question that recipients might not understand. Test this out during interviews at the pre-survey stage and again in pilot surveys.

- Use 'warm up' questions at the start of the survey. A few neutral questions at the beginning of a survey can ensure that the first real question is answered seriously.
- The survey report will reflect what people voted for on the day of the survey. If there are any big issues in the organisation at the time of the survey this will skew the results and should be taken into account in the question design and the analysis.
- Watch out for statements for which there is only one 'right' answer e.g. 'Safety is important to me'.

10.5 Validating The Answers

The most useful big ticket general cultural information usually comes from a small number of 'opinion' questions. It's key to capture any available data to validate the opinions expressed in the survey. Consider using information captured in the desk study to identify corroboration or dissention in the answers. Here are some tips:

- The first pilot survey is the starting point. Most valuable surveys shape up to something gradually more meaningful over time. Observing how people respond to the first survey report will lead survey writers to the next shaping step.
- Interviewing skills are invaluable. Interviews help explain why people answered survey questions as they did.
- Using the pilot survey results as the basis for interviews will help shape the next set of questions.
- Useful data will appear by asking small groups why people may have voted the way that they did. Asking for examples enables the group to expand on detail.
- In small group feedback sessions, people are likely to be cautious until they are sure that there will not be a bad reaction when they tell an unpleasant truth.

10.6 Feeding Back The Results

Some leaders respond very badly to their first survey report. About half of our climate surveys have received an initial poor response. This defensiveness sometimes manifests as denial, often of the validity of the survey.

An aggressive or 'only critical' response from a leader can mean that the initial survey was on target (if you are getting shot at, you must be doing something right). Some leaders insist on knowing 'who said what'. This must be resisted at all costs. Some even speak out in sarcastic tones about the survey results. It is paramount that leaders persistently reinforce the results when speaking with others. If they do anything else, the chance that they will hear the truth again in future are significantly diminished.

It's worth planning in the time to use the survey information for improvement immediately after the survey. Analysing, validating, checking, discussing and creating action plans all take time. If time is also made for the actions generated, it is possible to have a very fast turnaround from 'enquiry' to 'adjustment'. This fast response time is one of the many reasons to keep surveys short.

It's also always good for the leader to say 'thank you' to everyone and state that the survey was successful, especially if they promised that something new will happen following the survey results. Keeping people in the loop is easy to do, yet frequently neglected. Consider how the feedback gets back to the respondents. The mood created has to be increasingly upbeat and trusting. The people surveyed were good enough to state their opinions; it's important to give them feedback in a timely manner on each key concern. Sharing the full report with anyone that wants to read it will help to satisfy this need.

Only run as many surveys as the leadership team are prepared to act upon. Bear in mind that if the survey respondents see no changes over time as a result of the survey, they will quickly conclude that it is not important to the leaders and was therefore a waste of their time.

Do not try to fix everything highlighted in the survey all at once. Focus in on a few key changes that will be quickly visible to everyone, and work hard on those things. Communicate the change: Tell people briefly what the change is, why it is coming about (in this case, it was highlighted in the surveys) and what they can do to help it be successful.

10.7 Self-Surveys For Leaders

The previous section covered surveys aimed at analysing organisational performance, which is a barometer of overall leadership performance. Leaders may wish to analyse their personal performance. If this is the case, they might start by asking themselves some questions. These could include:

- I seek out dissenting opinion on safety issues when we plan our work: always/often/sometimes/rarely/never.
- My safety advisors are coaches not cops: yes/no.
- I coach my people one to one: daily/weekly/monthly/ yearly/never.
- The last conversation I had with a direct report focused primarily on: me/them/production/safety/something else.
- The last conversation I had with my boss focused primarily on: me/them/production/safety/something else.
- I am comfortable all our people get the support they need to challenge and reduce unnecessary bureaucracy: yes/no.
- I have done a really good job at supporting my people through their improvement plans: definitely/mostly/somewhat/not really.
- Our safety reporting processes focuses on enough leading indicators for us to be able to continuously improve: yes/no.
- I always return phone calls and emails within a reasonable time: yes/no.
- I always personally apologise to people if I have to cancel appointments: yes/no.

10.8 Strategic Leader Self-Survey

These questions are designed to form the basis for a coaching conversation regarding leadership. It is frequently the case that a leader will be scored less highly by her or her direct reports than they score themselves. Having an open conversation about this phenomenon helps leaders at all levels in a business understand how they are perceived and the disproportionate effect that a few seemingly small dysfunctions can have on the people around them.

Always = 5   Mostly = 4   Sometimes = 3   Rarely = 2   Never = 1

You

1. I _____ prepare for meetings.
2. I _____ plan to avoid delivering careless extinction.
3. I _____ scan for opportunities to demonstrate good leadership.
4. I _____ care about the people who work for me.
5. I _____ avoid letting my ego get in the way of good work relationships.
6. I _____ cut distracting corporate stuff off at the pass.
7. I _____ respond reasonably when I hear bad news.
8. If I have to cancel or postpone, I _____ do it personally.
9. I _____ look for things to praise.
10. I think I am _____ trusted by my people.

Total of your scores = (50 max)

Your Line Manager ('day to day' work line manager)

1. My manager _____ prepares for meetings.
2. My manager _____ plans to avoid delivering careless extinction.
3. My manager _____ scans for opportunities to demonstrate good leadership.
4. My manager _____ cares about the people that work for him/her.
5. My manager _____ avoids letting their ego get in the way of good work relationships.
6. My manager _____ protects me from distracting corporate stuff.
7. My manager _____ responds reasonably upon hearing bad news.
8. If my manager has to cancel they _____ do it personally.
9. My manager _____ looks for things to praise.
10. I think my manager is _____ trusted by his/her people.

Total of your manager's scores = (50 max)

11. Survey Feedback Essentials

Surveys result in a glut of feedback. Often, the feedback will be personal when it is about a leader or the environment that the leader has created. How this sensitive feedback is presented and delivered is key to bringing about successful improvements in production, safety and discretionary effects in the workplace. This chapter comprises tips on how to deliver or present feedback in a way that increases the chances it will successfully change behaviours.

11.1 Delivering Feedback

- Make sure a tested, robust relationship exists with the person you're delivering feedback to. People won't listen to or learn from feedback if they have a poor relationship with the person giving it.
- The feedback should be:
  - a. Factual.
  - b. Pinpointed.
  - c. About pinpointed behaviours, not quirks or traits.
  - d. Non-emotional.
- Consider the reason for this particular element of feedback. Is this being delivered for the recipient to improve a skill or for them to be aware of a distracting trait they exhibit?
- Keep the 4:1 ratio in mind. High-performing teams have a ratio of 5-6 positive feedback statements for every critical one made. If you find yourself giving equal amounts of positive to critical feedback to someone, the relationship may become strained quite quickly.
- Make sure you have enough credit in your feedback account. Each piece of critical feedback costs you a bit in terms of today's relationship with this person. Delivering positive feedback 'deposits' some credit into your account. People stop listening when you're consistently over-drawing your account.

- Use shaping. Sometimes shaping is necessary to get to the point of being able to deliver the piece of critical feedback (from both the giver and the receiver's perspective). Start by delivering smaller bits of critical feedback first, and building up to the highly critical things slowly. Just make sure you're delivering lots of genuine positive feedback in between!
- Make feedback informal and frequent. Feedback should be timely, and should be offered frequently in informal settings (hallways, meetings, e-mails). This makes getting feedback much less threatening and much more of a normal part of work.
- Give descriptive, pinpointed feedback, not scores out of ten. Scores are useless in terms of improving pinpointed behaviours over time.
- Don't make feedback sandwiches. People only remember the terrible tasting part.
- Know when to shut up. Sometimes people experience a lot of natural feedback as a result of their behaviour, especially if something has publicly gone wrong or resulted in failure. In those situations, most people don't need any external feedback to change their behaviour.

11.2 Receiving Feedback

- Punishing feedback is easy. Do not explain your behaviour when you receive feedback; it will come across as being defensive and will most likely punish the person giving you feedback. "Yeah, let me explain to you why I do that" is going to kill any future attempts at delivery of feedback.
- The golden rule is to say "thank you" when hearing feedback. It's a gift, so say thanks.
- If some of the feedback smarts a bit then remember that a lot of the most useful stuff always does. Still say "thank you" - you can dislike the person who delivered it after they have gone if you want a rationale to ease the pain.
- After thanking the person, wait for at least few minutes before responding further.

- Ask the right questions in response. Be specific about what you want from the feedback; are there any topics or behaviours you want feedback on more than others?
- Consider asking for a certain number of pieces of feedback at a time, or just one useful solitary piece.
- Ask for examples in order to assist your understanding of the feedback. Do not stray into any territory that might sound like you're being defensive.
- Ask for dissenting opinions of any ideas you have for a solution. This gives people permission to be critical of your idea. Remember to say "thank you."
- Be aware of your body language and facial expressions when receiving feedback; it doesn't take much to punish feedback. Asking for feedback and then acting as if it is unwelcome is another easy way to punish feedback.
- Reinforce honest feedback. A great way to reinforce feedback and make it more likely people will give you honest feedback in the future is to change the behaviour in question immediately, and to let them know you're trying.
- It's best not to ask for feedback at all if you have no intention of changing. Therapy only works for willing participants. If you ask for feedback and don't change, it feels patronising to the people being asked to provide feedback.

Delivering and receiving feedback well is a learned skill and takes practice. Feedback can be overt ("I liked when you said…") or more subtle (a smile or a raised eyebrow). For someone paying attention, the environment is full of all kinds of feedback. It's relatively rare for people to make the best use of it, but it is a powerful resource just waiting to be harnessed.

12. Safety Data Analysis - Bruce Faulkner

This chapter was devised and written by Bruce Faulkner. I trained in behavioural science and subsequently worked with Bruce introducing behavioural techniques for the Bechtel Corporation. He is now a leading behavioural consultant and was the joint founder of the BMT Federation. His work on data analysis is ground-breaking. In this chapter he explains that most important safety information is available to organisations within the workplace and is normally included in existing reporting regimes. However most companies do not properly analyse the information they already have to hand. Bruce contends that organisations' energies are frequently expended collecting and reporting information but effective analysis is rare. He also proposes some simple techniques for analysing data.

12.1 The Signal Is Already Present

Leaders in organisations are often surprised by sudden changes in safety performance. Typically, a major incident investigation seems to find evidence of declining standards over time. Patterns within the current safety reporting data are already present but sometimes they only show up as what we call 'weak signals'; they are hard to detect. Part of the problem lies in the typical organisation's approach to data handling.

Analysis of data with the goal of improving safety can feel a bit overwhelming, often impenetrable. This chapter contains some techniques designed to help narrow the focus of investigation. The goal is to wade through the noise, find a signal that matters and then make a meaningful change that will improve safety performance.

Narrowing the Focus

Noise   Signals   Changes

Time ➡

12.2 Surprises Happen

Organisations develop activities and processes aimed at preventing injuries and incidents. Monitoring mechanisms are created to provide assurance that the prescribed activities are happening. Forms get filled in, data is collected and results are reported.

The organisation also relies on people doing their part. Being trained in safe ways of working is only the beginning. The staff, supervisors and leaders all have to deliberately participate in safety. Each has to remain continually vigilant in order for the safe working environment to be created and sustained over time.

Consider the way people typically gain weight. From one day to the next it feels about the same. Over the course of a year, a few pounds can easily accumulate. Clothes get a bit tighter, you buy the next size up and think, "I must do something about that." It's the sneaky trap; change is occurring though a very gradual process. A systematic desensitisation to small changes in body weight has taken place.

This process is very similar to the one typically played out regarding safety assessments. Most of the items on the inspection list are complied with most of the time. When there is non-compliance it is usually the same basket of typical issues. The corrective actions are normally the same each time. The cycle repeats itself month on month. There is nothing out of the ordinary that would catch the eye.

To see this visually, examine some recent safety assessment scores. Take a sample of the last 20 to 30 assessment scores. A typical distribution will show 75-80% of the scores to be at or above the level of compliance. This means that most teams have figured out how to score well enough to avoid any confrontation. They will be avoiding the threat (R-, negative reinforcement) of a low score, which is not the same act as creating a safe place to work.

When an injury or serious safety incident occur it can feel like there has been an abrupt change in performance. One discrete event, a sudden drop in performance and safety is now seen as 'poor'.

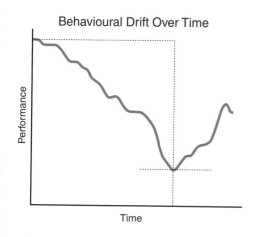

Behavioural Drift Over Time

Performance

Time

Obviously that does not reflect the whole story. Workers and supervisors, managers and leaders will have become systematically desensitised to small changes in safety performance over time. A downward behavioural drift will have set in long ago. The standards of what was accepted were in decline. People just hadn't recognised it was happening.

12.3 Passive Leadership Allowing Virtual Safety To Emerge

Having been desensitised, unless an incident or injury occur, it is inevitable that the daily distractions at work move the leadership focus away from real safety (competent supervision and obstacle removal) to virtual safety (removing today's threats). In this way, safety leadership becomes a passive and reactive activity.

With standards in a slow long-term decline, the staff and supervisors become conditioned to varying degrees of non-compliance as the workplace norm. There is a high probability that they will feel uncertain about the other inevitable and subtle indications of a decline in safety performance that haven't yet been detected by the leadership team.

12.4 Why Don't We See The Signal?

When displaying large quantities of information it is common to use a traffic light status system (red, amber, green). Some reports may compare performance to last month.

This style of reporting is focused on detecting the exceptions. If something is amber, leaders enquire if a corrective action is in place.

They are advised that everything will be back on track next reporting period. And it is. The whole setup feels predictable, reassuring and comfortable. Everyone knows what to expect. In reality, the key players at all levels are becoming increasingly desensitised. This reflects a culture where 'everything is OK until one day when it's not OK'.

Leaders actually need to know how workplace behaviour is changing over time: not month to month, but over 6 to 12 months. When the right information is displayed visually it is easy to see the trends. Performance over time is either getting better, remaining the same, or getting worse.

Despite the fact the safety reporting is most probably overly voluminous, organisations usually have more useful data than people realise. Also, to fix their problems leaders generally need less data than they think they do. But first, safety performance data must be put into context.

12.5 Understand Context By Looking To The Environment

A performance score or a result is produced through human behaviour. Human behaviour is primarily a product of its environment. This reflects what is called the extended results chain.

The Extended Results Chain

Environment ➡ Behaviour ➡ **Result**

Organisations typically focus most on the part of the chain that is well lit - the results, the lagging measures. But the results won't tell leaders anything about the current conditions in the environment. A singular focus on monitoring just the results leaves people blind to how the workplace environment is changing.

Take this scenario: A worker has been asked to deliver a result. They go to the workface and find a set of environmental conditions. They will now adapt their behaviour to those conditions and try to deliver the desired results. The workface is the place where the serious incidents and injuries typically occur.

The conditions in the local environment (in this case the workface) are always a result of decisions made by the leaders that are upstream from the person doing the task. If leaders are supplied with simple ways of understanding how the local environment is changing over time, they can intervene and reduce risk. Most commonly-used safety reporting models simply aren't sensitive enough to detect these crucial indicators of future potential problems.

12.6 Determining What Is Influencing The Local Environment

Safety data is usually voluminous, and examining all of it wouldn't be an effective or efficient use of time. This exercise helps narrow the focus to find the useful information: Get copies of the safety monitoring reports. List each activity that is being monitored on a separate post-it note. Sort these notes into three groups. The groups should be organised left to right in increasing level of impact on making the local working environment safer.

Organising the Search

Reporting	Actions Closed Out	Supervision
Statutory Inspections	Start of Shift Brief	Safe & Tidy
Site Safety Tours		Plant & Tools

→ Makes the local environment safer

Now pick 3 or 4 items from the right-hand side. These are the activities that have the most impact on preventing incidents and injury. Using the safety reports from the previous 6 months, create one graph for each item. Plotting the scores over time will show how performance has been changing.

If there is a downward trend then a warning signal has been detected.

12.7 Using The Signal To Change

The performance graph helps isolate a valuable activity or process that isn't functioning as expected. Recall; the original premise of this activity or process was to help prevent incidents. The environment is the primary source of environmental conditions that influences behaviours, so it is now important to understand which components of the working environment are contributing to the behavioural drift.

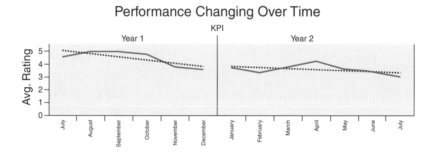

When people design a process they use their frame of reference to define the activities. They have to apply assumptions to the exercise. They anticipate the conditions, then plan out a sequence of events, and set out how workers will be organised to get the work done. In essence, the process-designers paint a picture that includes all of the environmental conditions that they think will probably exist when the work is being done.

Of course, work doesn't always proceed according to the original plan. Workplaces are dynamic places; things change. Sometimes the planning of activities runs late. Priorities are changed. All of this creates new and potentially unanticipated dynamics. There are increasing levels of uncertainty. Change within workplace environments is a major contributor to injuries and incidents.

Processes are built based on a set of assumed environmental conditions. Therefore processes are insensitive to changes in the environment. The people who are doing the work can observe all of the disconnects and the obstacles. In the short-term, people are highly sensitive to changes in their workplace environment.

Staff can always detect any change to what was anticipated, planned or organised. They could now be faced with something very different and they will customarily be expected to maintain production as planned. Using a bit of data and a workplace environmental analysis it is possible to narrow the focus and identify where safety performance can be improved. The next steps will describe how to shift leadership focus. When this shift occurs, safety leadership switches from passive to active and safety performance goes from virtual to real.

12.8 Using The Most Sensitive And Responsive Measurement Tool Available

The workface is where the serious incidents occur. It is the point of greatest exposure. The workers and staff there can serve as the dynamic measurement tool. They can always tell leaders if conditions are getting better, remaining the same, or getting worse, but many are rarely asked.

Good leaders already know that they have an incredibly accurate and sensitive safety measuring device at their disposal. It comes from the people with the most skin in the game, those closest to the workface. They know where the disconnects are between what the planned activities say should be happening and today's actual environmental conditions. They know when they are faced with increasing uncertainty. They know when they feel unsafe. They know when they feel safe.

Transforming the staff into a measurement tool is achieved by use of regular anonymous opinion surveys. Why anonymous? Because when people can express their opinion anonymously the threat of reprisal is removed. Research shows that when opinion data is collected anonymously the shift in reported opinion can be as much as a 50%. Most people are happy to speak out when they believe there is 0% chance of any subsequent reprisal.

As shown in the extended results chain, components in the environment have the most influence on behaviour and therefore results. The conditions required for human performance are well studied in behavioural science. Dr Ryan Olson has summarised the essence of this research in his performance equation (see chapter 8). He points out that the largest performance improvements comes first from removing obstacles.

Performance = (Motivation + Ability) - Obstacles

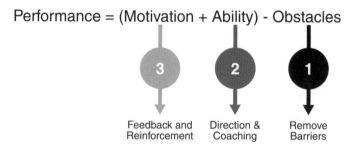

| Feedback and Reinforcement | Direction & Coaching | Remove Barriers |

Anonymous survey data can be analysed to create new knowledge about local obstacles. Linking the survey data with the workplace environmental analysis in order to isolate the activities and components that are obstacles to performance is the next step. This knowledge can then be used to make decisions and take action. The cause and effect relationships within safety performance will now become clearer.

Often, corporate reporting and analysis attempts to measure a whole host of different local environments. The executive leaders are aiming to deliver generic initiatives to 'fix' the whole company. This approach can never work alone, as the local environments will all be too different. The analyses outlined in this chapter should be carried out at a local level, with local leaders sufficiently educated and empowered to act on the findings. At a corporate level, a secondary analysis of all the local trends will help to identify enterprise level issues that, due to their common reoccurrence, are probably being driven by the executive leadership, and hence should be the focus of their efforts. Using these tools, safety improvement will no longer feel impenetrable.

A safe workplace is created by making mindful changes and monitoring to see if performance is getting better over time. It is important to continue to monitor lagging indicators of performance and use frequently solicited opinion as the leading indicator for decision-making. While opinions are subjective, a significant shift in the strength of opinion one way or another will indicate to a leader if their changes are having the desired effect. By regularly gathering the anonymous opinions of staff and workers, other areas of performance can be enhanced.

Leaders will know how well they are doing creating and maintaining safe working environments. It will be evidenced by the changes in the strength of opinion expressed by those surveyed. Opinions will always be the more sensitive and responsive measure in the extended results chain. This offers earlier opportunities to intervene before any behavioural drift sets in.

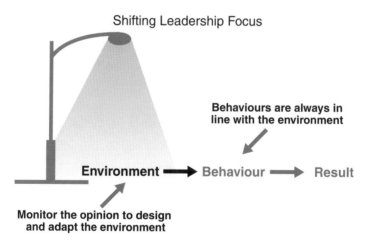

Shifting Leadership Focus

This new perspective of the extended results chain shows that the leadership focus has now shifted. Leaders now monitor opinion data in order to design and adapt the environment to reduce at-risk behaviours. Deliberately removing obstacles is an active demonstration of great leadership. Staff and workers now know safety is real because they can see their environment being changed for the better.

13. Conclusion

Much has changed since I pulled on my first pair of wellies on that Mowlem site in 1969. My career took numerous different paths that were directed mostly by various opportunities that sprang up along the way. My last proper job was a senior role at Bechtel, and that excellent company still puts safety front and centre. The leaders I worked for there were outstanding, and always exhibited a 'strong and caring' leadership style. These were the kinds of people everybody wants to work for - people with strength and integrity who will always look out for us and make us feel good about ourselves. These leaders realised the principle of 'create the right environment and watch them crops grow'.

Over the years I instinctively knew that leadership generates multiple contributory factors that affect your workplace, including the creation of a safe or unsafe workplace. These contributory factors also decide whether you will succeed, thrive, have fun and learn new skills, or fail, or get cheesed off and leave. One person in your environment can make all the difference. Take out a bad person and put in a good person and your whole life changes. Peter Block's term 'the helpless and distressed working for tyrannical boss' is great; the numbers of people who from time to time get consumed by one nemesis is astonishingly frequent.

My list of strong and caring leaders is getting longer. These are the people who hang on to their integrity and make the leap of faith that doing the right thing will mostly result in a happy ending. These are the people who work out how to remove the barriers, physical or human. These are the people who keep faith in their own ability, and frequently amass followers along the way. Their followers then pass these admirable qualities on to others, with everyone developing multiple excellent careers.

If you try something new out every day, keep the good stuff, and fail fast on the not-so-good stuff, then you will be improving over time. Great careers are developed over time; there are lulls and spurts. There will be frequent opportunities to go to the dark side. Please, recognise these for what they are, hang on to your integrity and do the right thing.

Howard Lees, Bollington, Cheshire, England, August 2017

Appendix A -
The Safety Continuum

The Safety Continuum is a measuring tool developed by the BMT Federation and featured in the Hollin book, *Behavioural Safety for Leaders*. It helps to identify different stages for an organisation's safety culture. There are five in total, ranging from poor to great. By using behaviours to describe the stages in a culture, it is possible for leaders to map their own company's culture. The mapping process not only encourages leaders to recognise their current behaviours, it also helps to identify the behaviours they need to exhibit in order to get to the next stage.

A typical journey

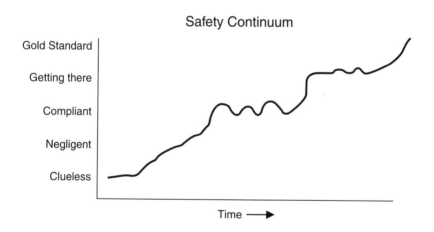

Clueless	Negligent	Compliant	Getting There	Gold Standard
Safety is not considered	Safety is avoided	Safety is a distraction	Safety is a priority	Safety is a value

CLUELESS - Safety is not considered

- At best, there is a hired-in external safety company to do the bare minimum legal requirements.
- Safety rules only appear in paperwork or posters.
- There are some signs on site.
- There are no records of injuries or incidents.
- There are never any tool box talks or start-of-shift briefings for workers.
- No director is named responsible for safety.
- There is no in-house safety advisor.

NEGLIGENT - Safety is avoided

- A blind eye is turned to knowledge of hazards, leaders are ignorant of legal requirements.
- An external safety company provides standard paperwork, notices, signs etc.
- Risks are taken to save short term money.
- Leaders are ignorant of safety non-compliance events and breaches.
- Whistle-blowing is impossible: People are punished when they report safety breaches or hazards.
- Leaders are passive regarding their lack of safety legislation knowledge.
- There are blatantly illegal activities occurring.

COMPLIANT - Safety is a distraction

- Procedures and processes are in place, and customised where necessary.
- There is an in-house safety advisor.
- There is more virtual safety than real safety.
- Safety advisors act as policemen.
- Safety is an item on meeting agendas.
- Incidents, injuries and other events that are reportable are recorded.
- Safety awards are sought.
- Sub-contractors must meet only minimum requirements e.g. simple self-assessment safety questionnaires.

- Sub-contractors' injuries and incidents not part of the overall statistics.
- Minor injuries and close calls are not reported.
- Archaic language is still used - e.g. accidents, near misses.
- There are 'Zero' targets.
- All measures are lagging indicators.
- No climate surveys take place.
- There is no training for supervisors on start-of-shift briefings or tool box talks.
- Safety is led by the safety department.
- There is a blame culture.
- A director is responsible for safety (also quality, the environment, HR perhaps).

GETTING THERE - Safety is a priority

- Safety climate surveys are carried out.
- A safety strategy is required by a client and developed and delivered by the contractor.
- A Board Director for Safety is appointed.
- Audits include behavioural elements.
- A behavioural training programme is in place.
- Supervisors are trained and measured on tool box talks/start-of-shift briefings, and communications.
- Safety tools are lean.
- Safety advisors act as coaches rather than police.
- The new language of incidents and close calls has been adopted.
- Close calls and minor injuries are recorded and trended.
- Measures include a balance of lagging and leading indicators.
- No longer seeking safety awards.
- Not yet trusting people to do the right thing.
- The safety performance of sub-contractors is verified and validated prior to procurement.
- There is one published set of safety statistics which includes sub-contractors and suppliers.
- Basic PPE is always in evidence.
- Blanket policies are in place on PPE items such as safety glasses, gloves and mobile phones.
- A large amount of potentially meaningless data is collected.

GOLD STANDARD - Safety is a value

- There are predictive safety KPIs.
- There is no specific Safety Director on the board.
- The safety department is small and lean.
- Safety is led by operational line management.
- BMT is rolled out to all staff.
- People regularly use behaviour analysis tools to help predict outcomes.
- Operational line management investigate all incidents and injuries.
- Operational line management write safety procedures.
- New technology is utilised.
- The performance of the supply chain is validated.
- There is Performance Management of contractors/sub-contractors.
- Safety standards are dictated by each distinct work group.
- Environments are designed to create safe working.
- There is peer-to-peer challenge on unsafe behaviours.
- Method statements are lean and written by distinct work groups.
- There is mindful fluency training.
- Managers and leaders frequently ask, "How is this decision going to affect safety?"
- Dynamic risk assessments are used.
- People often seek dissenting opinions.
- Improvement plans are evidence-based.
- No bonuses are paid for safety.
- Workplace environments are rich in feedback.

Appendix B -
Behaviourally Sound Safety Philosophy
For An Organisation

- We roll out behavioural safety courses to all our clients/supply chain - it is part of our overall behavioural safety and collaboration plan.
- We would never let safety governance take precedence over real safety - our safety processes have to be behavioural, believable and deliverable.
- We would never let virtual safety take hold - our people always know they are expected to do the right thing.
- Running through safety scenarios is part of our induction process.
- We don't have any measures like zero targets or man-hours without an LTI - those could punish the people who are behaving safely every day.
- We don't use the term 'accidents' - we call them 'incidents' and 'injuries' because genuine accidents are rare.
- We are happy to join in with our client/supply chain's objective safety measures, but we will argue strongly with those that want to use aversive or subjective measures on safety.
- We are not afraid to give feedback to our clients/supply chain when we discover they have safety problems.
- We spend the time and money to make sure that our safety message really gets through.
- We objectively rate our clients/supply chain on H&S.
- We have an accredited safety programme.
- Our foremen regularly solicit feedback from everyone involved in their projects.
- Our foremen write their own toolbox talks. They decide the format of start of shift briefings and they rate the supply chain supervision objectively.
- Our safety experts advise and coach rather than catch and fine.
- We don't drown our people with frequent voluminous 'all staff' emails.

Appendix C -
Behavioural Science Terms Used In This Booklet

Behavioural science is the science of human behaviour; it is founded on using data and analysis to come to conclusions about what is happening in the interactions of people. Objectivity is at the core of behavioural science. Behavioural Management Techniques (BMT) is a blend of behavioural science tools and project management skills.

I have written a booklet called *Notes on Behavioural Management Techniques* which discusses behavioural terms and offers more explanation than is covered here. This chapter should be enough to help you with the terms I mention in this booklet.

Psychologists seek to understand what is going on inside the mind, to modify these internal phenomena and in doing so achieve behaviour change. Behavioural scientists observe the behaviour, seek to modify the external environment - which is the only thing we really have influence over anyway - and in doing so, achieve behaviour change. Behavioural science sees each person as an individual who desires a totally unique set of reinforcers from their environment (their world).

Both mainstream psychology and behavioural science are used in seeking to change behaviour. Critically, behavioural science has a greater verifiable record of achieving this and is also far easier for people to learn and apply.

A number of scientific terms are used in this booklet. These are described here:

Antecedents
An antecedent is a request or prompt; something which is attempting to drive a particular behaviour. A sign that says 'don't smoke', a speed sign, and a plan detailing how you will deliver a project are all antecedents. Antecedents are quite poor at driving behaviour if they are not paired with consequences. We are all regularly bombarded with antecedents.

Some antecedents are very good at demanding our attention. I care about the weather forecast the day before I'm going on a long walk. I care about the flight information board when I'm flying somewhere. I check what day I have to put the bins out. I look at the fuel gauge in my car when driving. Unfortunately, many work-based antecedents do not have the desired effect. Procedures, safety rules, notice boards, minutes of meetings and requests by email will all work in part, but will only work well if paired with consequences.

Behaviour

Behaviours are 'what we say and do'. They are entirely objective and measurable. It is common to see lists of behaviours in organisations that include 'communicating' or 'trust'. These are not true behaviours, as they are subjective. In contrast, 'saying "hello" to the receptionist' is a behaviour. Behaviours should fulfil the pinpointing rules (see below).

BMT - Behavioural Management Techniques

Behavioural Management Techniques (BMT) is a unique blend of applied behavioural science tools and project management skills. The aim of BMT is to get people to do the right things because they want to, not because they have to.

Consequences

The impact of consequences is the primary influencer of our behaviour. What happens to us following our behaviour will affect the likelihood of us performing the same behaviour again under similar circumstances.

Behavioural science states that there are two main consequence types that result in a behaviour occurring/recurring or stopping. They are defined as Reinforcement and Punishment. These fundamental principles are as follows:

1. If behaviour is maintained or increases it has been subject to reinforcement (R+ and R-).
2. If behaviour reduces or stops it has been subjected to punishment (P+ and P-).

The consequence in each individual case is defined by its impact on behaviour. The four consequences are summarised below. More detail can be found in the Hollin booklet *Notes on Behavioural Management Techniques*.

R+ or Positive Reinforcement: I got something I liked following my behaviour (e.g. I feel pleasure).
R- or Negative Reinforcement: I avoided something I didn't want by carrying out the behaviour (e.g. I feel relief).
P+ or Punishment: I received something I didn't want following the **behaviour (e.g. I feel pain).**
P- or Penalty: I had something I wanted to keep taken off me following the behaviour (e.g. I feel denied).

A note on Punishment/Penalty: People often attempt to punish or penalise behaviours, but unless those attempts have actually worked to stop the undesired behaviour they cannot be defined as Punishment or Penalty.

Extinction

Extinction is the process of being ignored. It can be very painful if you are the recipient of it. It is also a useful tool to use if you wish someone's irritating behaviour to go away. A subset of extinction is the extinction burst, an emotional outburst of some kind (usually verbal). This usually occurs when the behaviour is receding, and is a good indicator that it is.

Environment

The environment is the immediate location of a person, be it in their office, living room, their car; wherever the behaviour is occurring. A person's behaviour is mostly driven by the consequences that have followed the behaviour (or similar behaviours) in the past. The environment will dictate the consequences you experience and this includes the other people in the room, office etc. Small changes in environment can result in significant changes in the behaviour of an individual. The environment affects us and we affect the environment.

For example, imagine an office full of people. Take one person out of the office and replace them with a different person and the environment has changed. The change could be very significant depending on who left and who came in.

Pinpointing

Pinpointing is the process used to make sure that a behaviour is described accurately. Something is pinpointed when it complies with all the following rules:

1. It can be seen or heard.
2. It can be measured or counted.
3. Two people would always agree that the same behaviour occurred or not.
4. It is active (something is occurring).

People who learn pinpointing can quickly develop skills which reduce the amount of assumption in their environment. This reduction of (sometimes destructive) assumptions increases the amount of informed comment, decision and discussion.

It is advisable to gather data on situations via observations and keep notes of who actually said/did what. This significantly reduces the chance of unnecessary conflict created by assumption.

Pinpointing is a very useful skill for business. Next time someone relates something to you, if you are unsure of the message you can say, "Can you pinpoint that for me please?"

Shaping

Shaping is a simple concept which is very difficult to master. It recognises that you can't get from step one to step ten in one vertical stride. You sometimes have to first write out steps two through nine and then carry them all out, one step at a time.

People sometimes tell me, "I want to say this to my boss." Before you say anything you need to predict the chances of it being received the right way by your boss. "Not very good," will often be the reply. Unfortunately, you have to shape to the goal you want to achieve, and this usually means a time-consuming set of steps which will shape the environment so that you can eventually say what you want to say and it will have the desired effect.

Shaping is not for the impatient, and a realisation that patience is the key can take time for some people. Sometimes, there is no other choice. You can't force the situation to move any faster so your options are slow shaping or nothing. Many very reinforcing tools we use these days do not help us forge a patient approach, e.g. email and voicemail. It is not naturally reinforcing taking the extra time to consider, "Is this the right thing to say? Does something else have to be achieved before I can say this and get what I want?"

Shaping is inherent in everything we learn. If you want to play an instrument, you repeat and adapt until you can play the tune. Anything that requires mastery requires repetition, reflection and adaptation. Putting a group of employees to work effectively and safely requires a leader to choose carefully who will work with whom. It requires trial and error to find the best combinations. Iteration is trying things out and seeing what the result is, adjusting and trying again - this is shaping, it works, it's the only thing that does work when building a team. This is how you succeed at getting all the right people on the bus, sat in the right seats.

Stimulus Control

Stimulus control is present when someone asks for something and they get it every time. Relationships where there is strong stimulus control are trusting on both sides; this is not an 'obedience' test but a set of circumstances where both people's reactions to requests made and fulfilled (or not) become predictable to the other over time. Setting up stimulus control takes time and it doesn't arrive and stay forever - it needs nurturing. Relationship development is vital for strong stimulus control.

Appendix D -
Further Recommended Reading

I like to read. In fact, I am the guy on the train reading a book while most of the other travellers are frantically trying to get their internet connection restored. These books are all packed with varied wisdom of some kind. There are a number of useful shorter publications you could download from our website (www.hollin.co.uk) should you wish to start with an entrée.

1. What Got You Here Won't Get You There - Marshall Goldsmith
2. Turn the Ship Around! - L David Marquet
3. Maverick - Ricardo Semler
4. Why Employees Don't Do What They're Supposed To Do - Ferdinand F. Fournies
5. Bringing Out the Best in People - Aubrey Daniels
6. The Hungry Spirit - Charles Handy
7. Coaching for Improved Work Performance - Ferdinand F. Fournies
8. Performance Management - Aubrey Daniels and James E. Daniels
9. The Sin of Wages - William Abernathy
10. Other People's Habits - Aubrey C Daniels
11. The Tipping Point - Malcolm Gladwell
12. Myself and Other More Important Matters - Charles Handy
13. Open Minds - Andy Law
14. Leading Change - John P Kotter
15. The Empowered Manager - Peter Block
16. The 20% Solution - John Cotter
17. Measure of a Leader - Aubrey C. Daniels and James E. Daniels
18. The Elephant and the Flea - Charles Handy
19. How the Mighty Fall - Jim Collins
20. Good to Great - Jim Collins
21. Body Language - Allan Pease
22. Experiment at Work - Andy Law

23. OBM Applied - Manuel Rodriguez, Daniel Sundberg, and Shannon Biagi
24. The Empty Raincoat - Charles Handy
25. Unlock Behaviors, Unleash Profits - Leslie Braksick
26. Built to Last - Jim Collins and Jerry I. Porras
27. On Writing - Steven King
28. Don't Shoot the Dog - Karen Prior
29. Learning Reinforcement Theory - Fred S. Keller
30. The Seven-Day Weekend - Ricardo Semler
31. The First 90 Days - Michael Watkins
32. How to Deal with Difficult People - Ursula Markham
33. The Leadership Pipeline - Ram Charan, Stephen Drotter and James Noel
34. Understanding Organisations - Charles Handy
35. The Principles of Scientific Management - F.W. Taylor

Appendix E -
Other Hollin Publications

All Hollin Publications are available at **http://www.hollin.co.uk/shop**

POWER COACHING
By Howard Lees
ISBN number 978-0-9575211-2-4

THE TOO BUSY TRAP
By Howard Lees
ISBN number 987-0-9575211-1-7

THE STEPS BEFORE STEP ONE
By Howard Lees
ISBN number 978-0-9563114-9-8

NOTES ON BEHAVIOURAL MANAGEMENT TECHNIQUES
By Howard Lees
ISBN number 978-0-9563114-1-2

IDEAS FOR WIMPS
By Howard Lees
ISBN number 978-0-9563114-6-7

HOW TO EMPTY THE TOO HARD BOX
By Howard Lees
ISBN number 978-0-9563114-4-3

HOW TO ESCAPE FROM CLOUD CUCKOO LAND
By Howard Lees
ISBN number 978-0-9563114-8-1

BEHAVIOURAL SAFETY FOR LEADERS
By Howard Lees and Bob Cummins
ISBN number 978-0-9563114-5-0

BMT SCORECARDS
By Howard Lees
ISBN number 978-0-9575211-1-7

BEHAVIOURAL COACHING
By Howard Lees
ISBN number 978-0-9563114-2-9

notes:

notes:

notes: